MW00565746

Experiments with
Electric Circuits

by Sid Antoch

ZAP Studio Instructional Publication

Experiments with Electric Circuits

© 2010 Sid Antoch   All rights reserved

ISBN-13: 978-1-935422-11-2
ISBN-10: 1-935422-11-1

Trademark Information

TEKTRONIX,TEK, and OpenChoice™ Desktop
are registered trademarks of Tektronix, Inc.

OrCAD®, PSpice®, and Capture®
are registered trademarks of Cadence Design Systems.

LTspice®, and Linear Technology®
are registered trademarks of Linear Technology.

Microsoft®, Windows®, Excel®, and Word®
are registered trademarks of Microsoft Corporation.

Texas Instruments® and TI®
are registered trademarks of Texas Instruments Corporation.

Pictures, drawings, and diagrams by Sid Antoch
Edited by Anna Antoch

Cover photos by NASA
        Hubble Space Telescope, May 2009.
        International Space Station's solar array panels, August 2008.

ZAP Studio LLC   PO Box 1150   Philomath, OR 97370

www.zapstudio.com

Introduction

Sid Antoch has taught electrical engineering circuits courses at Portland State University and Portland Community College, and electrical engineering technology courses at Portland Community College and Tektronix. This lab book is in part the result of this experience.

Experiments in this manual are intended for the laboratory component, or as a supplement to the laboratory component of an electrical engineering electric circuits course. The experiments emphasize the use of spreadsheets and simulation software. Several of the experiments refer to the specific application of a Tektronix TDS type oscilloscope to acquire experimental data. These may be omitted or modified if the lab does not have TDS type oscilloscopes.

Analysis suggestions are provided for each experiment. These may be used as is or may be modified by the instructor according to the lab curriculum requirements. Experiments may be selected according to the accompanying textbook and course emphasis.

Equipment List

Digital Oscilloscope with 10X probes, Function Generator, Digital Multi-Meter.
Solder-less Breadboard. Power Supply: 0-volts to 6-volts and 0-volts to ±15-volts.
Phase Tripler (refer to appendix 2). Computer with word processor, spreadsheet, simulation, and data acquisition software.

Parts List

Resistors: 8.2, 10, 47, four-100, 220, 330, three-390, 470, 680, 750, 820, three-1K, 1.2k.
Resistors: two-1.5k, 1.8K, 2.2K, 3.3K, 3.9K, two-4.7K, 6.8K, 8.2K, 10K, 12K, 15K, 18K, 22K.
Resistors: 33K, two-100K, two 150K, 1 Meg, 2.2 Meg, all ¼ watt, 5%.
Trim Pots: 100 Ω and 10 kΩ, one turn, breadboard mountable, ¼ or ½ watt.
Capacitors: 1 nF, two-10 nF, 22 nF, 47nF, two-100 nF, 1 µF (non-polarized), 5%.
Inductors: 10mH, three-100 mH (50mA),
Light bulb: Type 2182 (14 V, 80 mA).
Analog meter, 1 mA < 1000 Ω (or 100 µA < 10,000 Ω).
Transformer: 12.6 VAC center tapped.
Audio Transformer, 1000 Ω, center tapped, to 8 Ω, 200 mW.
Loudspeaker, 8 Ω, 200 mW minimum, (2 to 4 inch).
Op-amp: LM741 or uA741
Light Emitting Diode (LED).
Transistor: 2N3904.

Contents

Experiment 1: Electrical Resistance and the Resistor

Introduction

Ohm's law is the most fundamental equation in electric circuit analysis. It states that the amount of electric current flowing in a circuit is directly proportional to the voltage applied to the circuit, and inversely proportional to its resistance.

$$I = \frac{V}{R}$$ I is current in amperes, V is potential difference in volts, and R is resistance in ohms.

Resistors are used in electric circuits to control the flow of current. Resistors are commercially available which have a specific amount of resistance and power dissipation ability. The amount of resistance is usually marked on the resistor using a color code. The power dissipation is determined by the physical size of the resistor.

An "ohmmeter" is used to measure resistance. Most ohmmeters are part of an instrument that is also capable of measuring other electrical quantities, such as voltage and current. These are typically called "multi-meters", and since they usually have a digital display, they are called "digital multi-meters" or "DMM's" for short. To use the DMM you need to know how to set it to make the desired measurement (function), and how to set it for best accuracy (range).

Objectives

The purpose of this lab exercise is to learn how to measure resistance with the DMM. An error analysis will compare the measured resistor values to the labeled resistor values using a spreadsheet. In addition, you will measure the resistance of series and parallel combinations of resistors, and compare the results to theoretical calculations based on equations provided.

Series and parallel connections will be made using a solder-less breadboard. The object of this part of the exercise is to learn to use the breadboard. Theoretical knowledge of series and parallel resistor connections is not expected.

Resistance values are read using the color code given below.

Standard Resistor Color Code

Color	Value	Color	Value
Black	0	Blue	6
Brown	1	Violet	7
Red	2	Gray	8
Orange	3	White	9
Yellow	4	Gold	0.1 / 5%
Green	5	Silver	0.01 / 10%

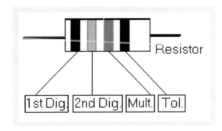

1st Dig. 2nd Dig. Mult. Tol.

Resistor

This color code is for "standard" resistors with an accuracy rating, or "tolerance", of ±5% or ±10%. That is, their value is guaranteed to be within ±5% or ±10% of their labeled value.

Their colors are read from left to right. The first two color bands represent the first two significant digits of the resistor value. The color of the third band represents a multiplier of 10^N, where N is the value represented by the color.

The fourth band is always gold or silver, which indicates a tolerance of ±5% or ±10%. The first band is never gold or silver. *So to read a resistor's value correctly, the gold or silver band must be on the right.*

For example, a resistor whose first band is red, second band is yellow, third band is orange, and fourth band is gold, has a value of 24,000-ohms (24×10^3), and a tolerance of 5%.

Resistance Measurement

A digital multi-meter (DMM) will be used for measuring the resistance values. The instructor may explain the operation of the instrument before you use it for the first time. You may also check to see if an instruction manual is available for the instrument. The DMM will have buttons and/or switches to set its function and range.

Set the function to "OHMS". Some meters are capable of automatically setting the range to get the most accurate reading, which is related to the number of significant digits displayed. You should be able to get at least three significant digits of accuracy. Experiment with the range settings when making the measurements specified in the procedure below.

The power rating of each resistor is determined by its physical size. Smaller dimensions represent a smaller power handling capability. A sample of several different size resistors should be available in the lab. A very common power rating is ¼ watt. If a ¼ watt resistor dissipates more than ¼ watt it will get excessively hot and may burn out.

Procedure

Equipment and Parts

DMM and Breadboard.
Resistors: 1K, 4.7K, 10K, ¼ watt, 5% or 10% tolerance.

Part 1: Measurements and the Spreadsheet

Do not touch the metal tips of the DMM probes when making measurements.

---

1.   Use the resistor color code to select the 1K, 4.7K, and 10K resistors. Determine their tolerance. Measure the values of the resistors with the DMM to at least three significant digits.

2. Enter the results into a spreadsheet. Calculate the deviation of each resistor's measured value compared to its labeled value. Calculate the percent deviation of each resistor's measured value compared its labeled value.

Use the spreadsheet layout shown below to do the calculations.

	A	B	C	D	E	F
1	Resistor	Labeled Val.	Measured Val.	Deviation	Labeled %	Measured %
2	1	1000				
3	2	4700				
4	3	10000				
5						
6						

Deviation: =C2-B2   Percent deviation: =(D2/B2)*100
Enter the expression for deviation into cell D2 and percent deviation into cell E2. Use the "fill down" feature of the spreadsheet to calculate rows 3 and 4.

Part 2: Series and Parallel Connections

Before starting this exercise (and the other exercises in this manual) you need to have a way of connecting electronic parts together into a circuit. An easy and very common method to quickly connect parts together is to use the "solder-less breadboard", also called a "prototyping board" or "protoboard". The board has holes 0.1 inches apart into which component leads can be inserted.

Solder-less breadboards are available from a variety of manufacturers and sources, in a variety of sizes, but they all have the same arrangement of the holes and connections

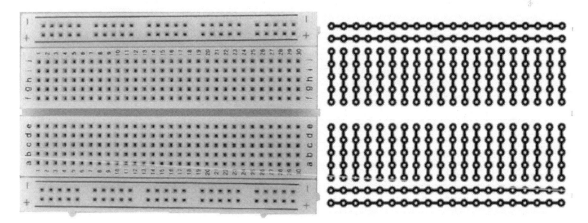

The picture above on the left shows a typical breadboard. Components such as resistors, capacitors, transistors, integrated circuits, and wires can be plugged into it. The picture above on the right shows how the holes are connected. You should memorize these connections.

Components such as resistors can be connected in series, parallel, and in a combination of series and parallel. The following exercises show how to connect resistors in series and parallel and measure the resistance of the series and parallel combinations.

The measurements will be compared to the theoretically expected values using the equations provided. If a measurement does not agree with the calculation, check the breadboard connections and the labeled values of the resistors.

1. Connect your 1K, 4.7K and 10K resistors in series. Measure and record the resistance, R_{TS}, of the series combination as shown in the circuit's schematic diagram below. A connection example is shown on the right.

    Ohmmeter leads connect between points a and b.

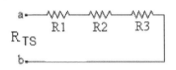

    R_{TS} _____ (measured total series resistance)

2. Calculate the theoretical resistance of this series combination with the equation:

    $$R_{TS} = R1 + R2 + R3.$$

    Use the measured values of the resistors from part 1. Enter the equation into your spreadsheet and have the spreadsheet do the calculation. Also enter the measured value into the spreadsheet as shown in the example spreadsheet on the next page.

3. Connect the 1K, 4.7K and 10K resistors in parallel as shown in the diagram below and picture on the right. Measure and record the resistance, R_{TP}, of the parallel combination.

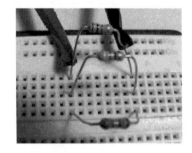

    Ohmmeter leads are connected between points a and b.

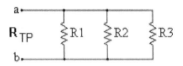

    R_{TP} _____ (measured total parallel resistance)

4. Calculate the resistance of this parallel combination using the equation below.

    $$\frac{1}{R_{TP}} = \frac{1}{R1} + \frac{1}{R2} + \frac{1}{R3} \quad \text{so that} \quad R_{TP} = \frac{1}{\left(\frac{1}{R1} + \frac{1}{R2} + \frac{1}{R3}\right)}$$

Use the measured values of the resistors from part 1. Enter the equation into your spreadsheet and have the spreadsheet do the calculation. Also enter the measured value of the series resistance and the measured value of parallel resistance into the spreadsheet as shown in the example spreadsheet below.

	A	B	C	D	E	F
1	Resistor	Labeled Val.	Measured Val.	Deviation	Labeled %	Measured %
2	1	1000	996	-4	0.05	-0.4
3	2	4700	4760	60	0.05	1.276595745
4	3	10000	9720	-280	0.05	-2.8
5						
6						
7		Calculated Val.	Measured Val.	Deviation	% Deviation	
8	Series	15476	15390	-86	-0.555699147	
9	Parallel	759.3125376	762.2	2.8874624	0.380273246	
10						

Equation in B8: =C2+C3+C4   Equation in B9: =1/(1/C2+1/C3+1/C4)

LAB REPORT

1.   Open a word processor document and save it as: "Experiment 1 Report". Use the following format:

Student name and lab partner name (if applicable).
Course number: Lab experiment number and name.

Example:

George Jones and Sally Smith

ENGR221: EXPERIMENT 1: Electrical Resistance and the Resistor

2.   Copy your spreadsheet results and paste them into the document.

The instructor will specify how to turn in the report. You may just need to show the resulting document on the lab computer, or the instructor may also ask for additional analysis, including a more comprehensive lab report.

Experiment 2: Voltage, Current, and Power

Introduction

Electrical devices which do work consume energy. Power is the rate that energy is consumed. Equations describing the relationship between power, energy, voltage, and current are given below. P is power in watts, W is work (energy) in joules, I is in amperes, and V is in volts:

$$P = \frac{dW}{dt} \qquad P = IV \qquad V = IR$$

All electric power sources are basically sources of potential difference or voltage. Examples include batteries, generators, solar cells, and power supplies.

A typical lab power supply has variable (adjustable) voltages from 0 to about 30 volts at a maximum current of about 1 ampere. Maximum ratings are often printed on the front panel. Note what maximum voltages and currents are available from your power supply. You may refer to the instrument's manual, if available, for more details.

Voltage Sources

Voltage sources used in circuit analysis are usually "ideal" sources. By ideal we mean that the value of the voltage of the source does not change regardless of how much current it supplies. Practical sources are limited in the amount of current they can supply.

A voltage regulated power source will supply a constant output voltage, V_S, when the output current, I, is less than its maximum limit, I_{lim}. Some power supplies have an adjustable current limit, I_{lim}, and they will supply a constant output voltage for load currents less than I_{lim}. Refer to the graph below.

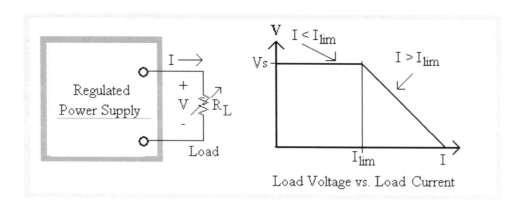

Load Voltage vs. Load Current

A power supply will be used to supply power to a light emitting diode (LED) in part 1 and to a light bulb in part 2. The voltage versus current characteristics and power dissipation of both will be measured and compared.

Voltage Measurement

The DMM will be used to measure voltage. *To measure voltage the meter leads are connected across (in parallel with) the device.* Voltage is measured between two nodes. Voltage is a potential difference. You are measuring the potential difference between two nodes.

Current Measurement

To measure current the meter must be connected in series with the circuit so that the current flowing through the ammeter is the same as the current flowing through the circuit. The circuit must be temporarily disconnected to insert the ammeter in series with it.

Current can also be determined by measuring the voltage drop across a known resistance and calculating the current flowing through it using Ohm's law. Current through an LED and an incandescent lamp will be determined from the voltage measured across a series connected resistor.

Objectives

The voltage versus current graph of a resistor is a straight line. The resistance of a resistor is constant and does not change with the current through it. This experiment will show that this is not the case for LEDs and light bulbs. Objectives of this exercise include gaining experience with voltage measurement, spreadsheet calculations, and spreadsheet graphing.

Procedure

Equipment and Parts

Power supply, DMM, and Breadboard
Resistors: 10 Ω and 1000 Ω (1/4 watt, 5%).
Light bulb: Type 2182 (14 V, 80 mA). Light Emitting Diode (LED).

Part 1: I versus V for an LED

1. Connect the circuit below. The positive lead of the LED is the anode. It is the longer lead and it should be connected to point A on the diagram below. Turn on the power supply and set the voltage to zero. Set the DMM function to volts and set the range to 20-volts.

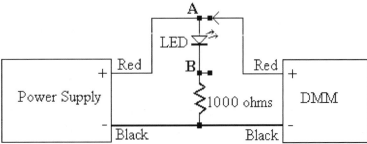

2.   The red DMM lead will be moved between points A and B follows:

(a)   Set the power supply voltage to exactly 0.0 V (as read on the DMM). The DMM's red lead should be connected to point A.

(b)   Move the DMM's red lead to point B. Measure and record the voltage at B.

(c)   Repeat steps (a) and (b) for voltages at point A of:
        1.0, 2.0, 3.0, 4.0, 5.0, 6.0, 7.0, 8.0, 9.0, 10.0, 11.0, 12.0 V.

Create a spreadsheet table as shown below. You will have 13 rows of data.

	A	B	C	D	E
1	Volts at A	Volts at B	Volts LED	A LED	Watts LED
3	0	0	0	0	0
4	1				
5	2				

C4 has: =A4–B4   D4 has: =B4/1000   E4 has: =C4*D4

You can automatically fill a column of data. For example, select cell C4 and then click the mouse on the bottom right corner of the cell, and drag the mouse down to fill all of the rows of that column.

Part 2: I versus V for a Lamp

1.   Connect the circuit below. The lamp is not "polarized". Its leads can be connected in either direction. Make sure that the power supply output voltage is set to zero. Set the DMM function to volts and set the range to 20 V.

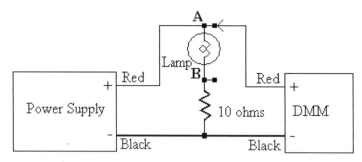

2.   The Red DMM lead will be moved between points A and B as follows:

(a)   Set the power supply voltage to exactly 0.0 V (as read on the DMM). The DMM's red lead should be connected to point A.

(b)   Move the DMM's red lead to point B. Measure and record the voltage at B.

(c)   Repeat steps (a) and (b) for voltages (as read by the DMM at point A) of:
        1.0, 2.0, 3.0, 4.0, 5.0, 6.0, 7.0, 8.0, 9.0, 10.0, 11.0, 12.0 V.

8

Create a spreadsheet table as shown below. You will have 13 rows of data.

	A	B	C	D	E
1	Volts at A	Volts at B	Volts Lamp	A Lamp	Watts Lamp
3	0	0	0	0	0
4	1				
5	2				

C4 has: =A4–B4   D4 has: =B4/10   Cell E4 has: =C4*D4

Analysis

1. Use the spreadsheet to graph the current versus voltage characteristics of the LED. Current is on the vertical axis and voltage is on the horizontal axis. Label the graph.

2. Use the spreadsheet to graph the current versus voltage characteristics of the lamp Current is on the vertical axis and voltage is on the horizontal axis. Label the graph.

3. The resistance of the device at a point on the graph is equal to the value of the voltage divided by the value of the current at that point. Use the spreadsheet to calculate the resistance at each point in column F.

   Plot the resistance of the LED as a function of power dissipation using your spreadsheet data (resistance on vertical axis).

   Plot the resistance of the lamp as a function of power dissipation using your spreadsheet data (resistance on vertical axis).

4. Copy each properly labeled graph and paste it into a word document. Your document should have the form below:

   Your Name   Course Number   Date   Experiment Number and Name

   Circuit diagrams with labeled voltages and currents
   LED Current versus Voltage Graph
   Lamp Current versus Voltage Graph
   LED Resistance versus Power Graph
   Lamp Resistance versus Power Graph

   Brief summary (what you learned from this exercise).

   The above is a short report. The instructor will specify how to turn in the report. The instructor may also ask for additional analysis, including a more comprehensive lab report.

Experiment 3: Analog D'Arsonval Meter

Introduction

An analog meter uses magnetic fields to measure electric current. A coil of wire wound on a bobbin creates a magnetic field whose strength is proportional to the wire's current. The bobbin is suspended in between the magnetic field of a permanent magnet as shown in the illustration on the right. The bobbin and attached needle rotate due to the magnetic force between the bobbin and the permanent magnet.

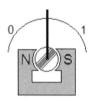

The wire winding has a resistance which determines one of the meter's characteristics. For example, if the winding resistance is 1000 Ω, and one milliamp causes "full scale" deflection, its "sensitivity" will be given as "1000 ohms per volt". By Ohm's law, 1 volt applied to 1000 ohms will create a current of one milliamp.

So a 1000 Ω, one-milliamp meter is also a voltmeter whose full scale voltage is 1 volt. The voltage range of the meter can be changed to 10 volts by adding a series resistance that will result in a one milliamp current when the applied voltage is 10 volts. The total resistance required to limit the current to 1 milliamp is 10,000 ohms. Connecting a 9000 Ω resistor in series with the meter makes the meter a voltmeter whose range is zero to ten volts.

Objectives

Measure the operating characteristics of an analog milliammeter. Use the measured meter characteristics to design a dual range analog voltmeter. Evaluate the performance of the voltmeter.

Procedure

Equipment and Parts

Power supply, DMM and Breadboard.
Analog meter, 1 mA < 1000 Ω (or 100 µA < 10,000 Ω).
R1: 1k, ¼ watt, 5% for 1 mA meter (or 10k, ¼ watt, 5% for 100 µA meter).
Values of resistors R2 and R3 to be determined.

Part 1: Meter Characteristics

1. Measure and record the value of R1. R1 is the 1k resistor if using a 1 mA meter (or 10k if using a 100 µA meter). Set the power supply voltage to zero. Connect the circuit on the right. Vs is a variable power supply (0 to 10 V). Connect the DMM to read the voltage, Vm, across the meter.

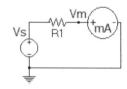

    R1 _____

2.	Slowly increase the voltage, Vs, until the analog meter reads full scale. Your eye should be directly above the meter's needle to reduce "parallax error". Measure and record the voltage, Vm, across the meter. Connect the DMM to Vs. Measure and record Vs.

Vm _____			Vs _____

3.	Calculate the actual meter current, I_{ma}, and resistance, R_{ma}, using the voltages, Vm and Vs, and the measured value of R1.

$$I_{ma} = \frac{Vs - Vm}{R1} = \underline{\hspace{3cm}}$$ 		$$R_{ma} = \frac{Vm}{I_{ma}} = \underline{\hspace{3cm}}$$

Part 2: Meter Design

1.	Use the calculated values of I_{ma} and R_{ma} from part 1, step 3, to design a dual range voltmeter circuit, as shown on the right, to measure 1 V full scale and 10 V full scale. Calculate the required values R2 and R3.

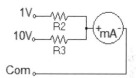

R2 _____		R3 _____

Use a series combination of resistors for R2 and R3 so that the resistors used in the circuit have measured values within 1% of the calculated values. Use a high value and low value resistor in series.

For example, if R2 = 930 Ω, you could connect the standard values of 910 Ω and 22 Ω in series to obtain 932 Ω. The percent error for this combination is:

$$\% \, Error = \frac{932 - 930}{930} \times 100\% = 0.215\%$$

Measure the resistance of your series combination. You may need to try another combination if your measured resistance is not within 1% of the required resistance. Note that 1% of 1000 Ω is equal to 10 Ω.

2.	Test the voltmeter circuit by comparing the analog meter readings to the DMM readings as follows:

a)	Connect the DMM to the variable power supply. Connect the 1 V input range of the analog meter (R2) to the variable power supply. The meters will be in parallel.

b)	Carefully set the power supply voltage so that the analog meter reads 0.20 V. Observe the analog meter reading from directly above the needle to minimize parallax error.

c) Read the voltage on the analog meter. Record the result in the table below.

d) Repeat steps (b) and (c) for voltages of 0.40, 0.60, 0.80, and 1.00 V.

e) Repeat the procedure for the analog meter's 10 V range and record results in the table below (for 2.0, 4.0, 6.0, 8.0, and 10.0 V).

1 VOLT RANGE			10 VOLT RANGE		
Analog Meter	DMM	% Error	Analog Meter	DMM	% Error
0.2			2.0		
0.4			4.0		
0.6			6.0		
0.8			8.0		
1.0			10.0		

Analysis

1. Calculate the sensitivity of the analog voltmeter in ohms per volt on the 1 V and 10 V range.

2. Calculate the input resistance of the analog voltmeter on the 1 V and 10 V range.

3. Calculate the percent error for all of the readings and record the results in the table. You could use a spreadsheet to do the calculations.

4. Calculate the average percent error of the analog meter on the 1 V and on the 10 V range.

5. Assuming that the analog meter is as accurate as the digital meter, calculate the voltage that each meter would read across the 15k resistor given that the digital meter has resistance of 1 megohm and the analog meter has a resistance of 10k ohms. Calculate the percent error for each meter.

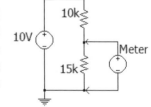

6. Use the values of I_{ma} and R_{ma} of the meter to design an analog ammeter with a full scale deflection current of 100 mA. Calculate the required value of the shunt resistance (resistance in parallel with the meter). What is the net resistance of the 100 mA meter (shunt resistance in parallel with the meter resistance, R_{ma}).

Experiment 4: DC Measurements and Meter Loading

Introduction

Meters used to measure voltage or current have an internal resistance. Since the meter must be connected to the circuit to make a measurement, the circuit is changed by the resistance of the meter. This is referred to as the meter's "loading effect".

Most meters have amplifiers built in so that only a small amount of power is needed from the circuit, and the loading effects are minimized. But this is not always the case.

A voltmeter is connected in parallel with the circuit across which the voltage is being measured. The loading effect of the meter will be minimal if the meter resistance is much larger than the circuit resistance. Ideally, the voltmeter resistance should be infinite. Practically, most electronic voltmeters (DMM's) have a resistance of 10 megohms.

The effect of the voltmeter resistance, Rm, across a circuit element, Rc, can be calculated using the parallel resistor equation:

$$Rt = \frac{Rc \cdot Rm}{Rc + Rm}$$

An ammeter is connected in series with the circuit in which the current is being measured. The loading effect of the meter will be minimal if the meter resistance is much smaller than the circuit resistance. Ideally, the ammeter resistance should be zero. Practically, the resistance of most electronic ammeters (DMM's) varies with the range setting, with the highest ranges having the least resistance. This is one case where setting the range for the most significant digits may not always result in the most accurate reading.

The effect of the ammeter resistance, Rm, in series with circuit element, Rc, can be calculated using the series resistor equation:

$$Rt = Rc + Rm$$

Even if the meter loading effect is insignificant there will be an uncertainty in the measured value due to measurement errors caused by the accuracy of the meter.

Objectives

A series-parallel circuit will be connected on a solder-less breadboard. Voltage and current measurements will be made on the circuit and the results will be compared to theoretical expectations. The effect of the resistance of the meter will be determined.

Procedure

Equipment and Parts
DMM, Power Supply, and Breadboard. Resistors: 100, 220, 1 Meg, 2.2 Meg, ¼ watt, 5%.

Part 1: Voltage Measurement

1. Measure and record the values of the resistors in the circuit. You will use these measured resistor values for your calculations and for *PSpice* input in experiment 5 and LTspice input in experiment 6.

    R1 _____   R2 _____

    R3 _____   R4 _____

2. Connect the circuit below on the left and set the power supply voltage to 6.0 volts.

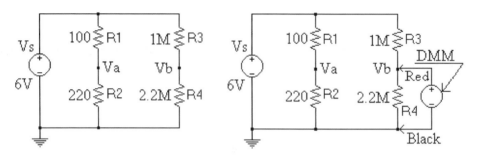

.   Lay out the circuit so that it looks similar to the schematic diagram. Use the minimum number of wires to connect the circuit.

      The positive power supply lead is connected to the top of R1 and the negative power supply lead is connected to the bottom of R2.

      The voltmeter is connected across R4.

3. Measure and record Va, Vb and Vab
    (Vab = Va – Vb)

    Va _____   Vb _____   Vab _____

4. Obtain and record the internal resistance, Ri, of your voltmeter. Ri _____

Part 2: Current Measurement

1. The circuit on the right shows the DMM connected in series with the 100 Ω and 220 Ω resistors. You need to break the connection between R1 and R2 and insert the meter as shown. The meter will read the current through the 100 Ω and 220 Ω resistors.

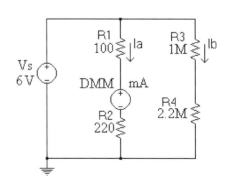

2. The internal resistance of a DMM on the current ranges varies with the range. Check the manual on your DMM to see what its internal resistances are on the current ranges. If you don't have a manual, your instructor should provide the information.   Record the meter resistances below.

    Rm(0.2 mA) _____   Rm(2 mA) _____

    Rm(20 mA) _____   Rm(200 mA) _____

3. Measure and record the current through the 100 Ω and 220 Ω resistors with the meter on the 20 mA range.

    Ia_{20} _____

4. Measure and record the current through the 100 Ω and 220 Ω resistors with the meter on the 200 mA range.

    Ia_{200} _____

Analysis, Part 1

1. Calculate the theoretical values of the voltages: Va, Vb, and Vab, without taking the meter resistance into account. Calculate the percent error between the theoretical and measured results.

2. Calculate the voltages: Va, Vb, and Vab taking the meter resistance into account. Calculate the percent error between the measured and calculated results.

Analysis, Part 2

1. Calculate the theoretical current, Ia, (without taking the meter resistance into account). Calculate the percent error between the theoretical and measured values (both current ranges).

2. Calculate the current, Ia, taking the meter resistance into account. Calculate the percent error between the calculated and measured results.

3. Briefly explain the significance of the error analysis in steps 1 and 2 above.

Experiment 5: PSpice Circuit Simulation

Introduction

This exercise will go through the steps of simulating the circuit of experiment 4. The software used is in two parts. "OrCAD Capture" is used to enter the schematic diagram. The circuit is then simulated using "OrCAD PSpice". The schematic diagrams and simulation results may be copied and pasted into other applications.

There may be some variation in the software interface depending on which version of PSpice is being used. "Help" is available within the program and online.

Drawing the Circuit

1. Start the "Capture" program. In the main menu bar, click on File. Select *New* and then *Project*. The [New Project] dialog box shown on the right will open.

2. Create the new project using: *Analog or Mixed A/D*.

3. Name the project and specify a saving location, as shown. Save project to a folder with the name of the project. You can copy that folder to another disk if you wish to run the simulation on another computer. Click on *OK*.

4. Select *Create a blank project* in the next dialog box.

5. After clicking *OK*, you can start drawing your schematic diagram.

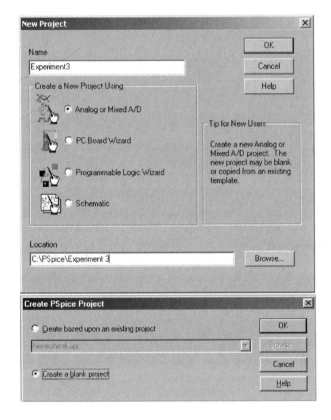

6. Note that some versions of "OrCAD Capture" startup slightly differently. You may get a dialog box asking you to select the libraries to use in your project. Be sure to select only the PSpice libraries.

   After selecting the libraries you can start drawing your circuit. Click on the blank workspace to start.

7. You should see a column of buttons on the right side of the screen. The ones you will use most often are shown here on the right. The first button, which is shown selected, allows you to select parts in your drawing by clicking on them. The parts change color when selected.

8. The second button is used to get parts for your schematic diagram. The third button is used for drawing wires. The fourth button, N1, is used to label nodes in your circuit. The last button, GND, is used to place ground references in your diagram. These four buttons are the ones most often used in drawing a circuit schematic diagram.

9. Click on the parts button. In the [Place Part] dialog box, click on *ANALOG* and select "R" from the parts list, as shown on the right.

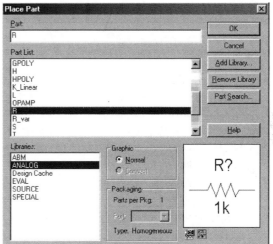

10. When you click on *OK* the dialog box will disappear, and you will be able to place the resistor into your diagram by using drag and drop. You can place multiple resistors into your diagram. The resistors are automatically numbered, starting with R1. The default value is 1k ohms.

11. Get four resistors, R1, R2, R3 and R4.

Place them into your diagram oriented vertically. The resistors and other parts may be rotated by clicking the right mouse button while the resistor is selected and clicking on *Rotate*.

The part references (R1, R2, R3, and R4) may be changed by double clicking on the part references. The part values may be changed by double clicking on the part values. Any selected item may be moved by dragging and dropping.

12. Get the part "VDC" from the source library and change its value to 6Vdc. Change the values of the resistors to the values measured in experiment 3. In PSpice, $M = 10^{-3}$ *and Meg* $= 10^6$. Click on the "wiring" button on the right side to connect the parts with wires. You should experiment with moving the parts and connecting the wires.

Try to make the circuit look like the one below. The ground symbol is obtained by clicking on the GND button, selecting *SOURCE* and selecting "0" as shown on the next page. The circuit will not simulate without the ground.

Schematic Diagram

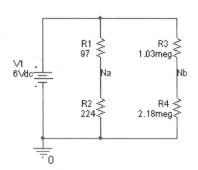

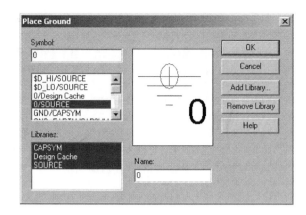

Simulating the Circuit

1. To simulate the circuit, click on PSpice and then on New Simulation Profile. You can also use the shortcut buttons. Note the menu bar below and note the button: New Simulation Profile. The next button is to Edit Simulation Profile. The third button (right arrow) is used to start the simulation.

New Simulation Profile ⬆   ⬆Edit Simulation Profile

2. The simulation was named "Bias Point" as shown on the right. After naming the simulation and clicking on *Create* you will get a [Simulation Settings] dialog box. "Analysis type" is set to *Bias Point*. Bias point analysis outputs the voltages at all of the nodes as well as the currents supplied by the power supplies.

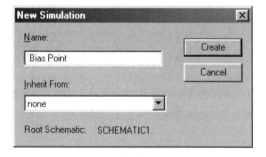

Results are available in an "Output File" which is generated for all simulations.

3. Refer to the [Simulation Settings] dialog box on the right.

4. Simulate the circuit by clicking the simulation button (arrow in main menu bar).

    Click on View and then on *Output File* in the window that opens. Scroll down until you get the voltages at the nodes, as shown below.

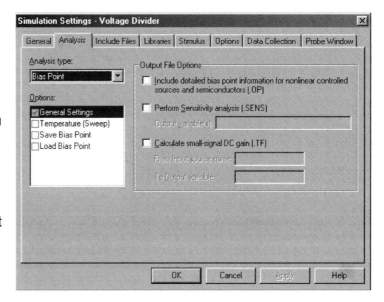

NODE   VOLTAGE   NODE   VOLTAGE   NODE   VOLTAGE
(NA)   4.1869   (NB)   4.0748   (N00149)   6.0000

VOLTAGE SOURCE CURRENTS
NAME   CURRENT
V_V1   -1.869E-02

5. Voltages can be displayed on the schematic diagram by clicking on the V button in the main menu. Currents can displayed on the schematic diagram by clicking on the I button in the main menu. Note the results below.

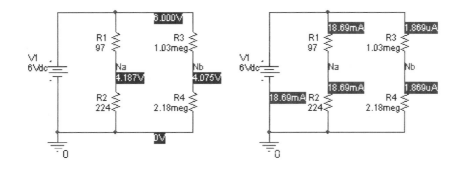

6. Record simulation results below.   Vab = Va – Vb.

    Va _____   Vb _____   Vab _____

    Ia _____   Ib _____

7.   Connect a 10 meg resistor in parallel with R4 to simulate the effect of the voltmeter. Run PSpice and record the result below.

Vb _____

8.   Connect a resistor whose value equals the resistance of the milli-ammeter on the 20 mA range between R1 and R2 to simulate the effect of the milli-ammeter. Run PSpice and record the result below.

Ia _____

Analysis

Present your measured results from experiment 4 and your simulated results from this exercise in a spreadsheet table. Have the spreadsheet calculate the percent differences between the measured and simulated results.

Cadence OrCAD PSpice is a very powerful program with lots of features. One way to learn more about how to use it is to use the "Help" in the main menu. There are also many reference books published on Spice and OrCAD PSpice.

Experiment 6: LTspice Circuit Simulation

Introduction

LTspice IV is similar to OrCAD PSpice and is easy to use. It is free to download from Linear Technology: http://www.linear.com/designtools/software/

You can also download a manual and a "getting started guide". One advantage over the evaluation version of OrCAD PSpice is that there are no limits on schematic size or number of components used. It is also used at many schools and universities.

Drawing the Circuit

1. Start the *LTspice* program. In the main menu bar, click on File and select New Schematic.

2. Create the new schematic. Left click on the "resistor" symbol and drag and place the resistor, R1.   Get three more resistors and place them as shown on the right.

    Right click on the "*R*" of each resistor. Change the values to the measured values from Experiment 4.

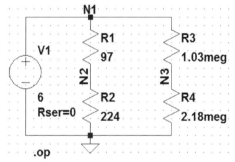

3. Left click on the gate symbol between the diode and the hand in the main menu to get the dialog box on the right. Select the part "*voltage*" and place it in the schematic.

    Click on the ground symbol and place it under R2.

4. Left click on the pencil in the main menu to connect the components.

5. Left click on the *A* between the ground symbol and the resistor symbol to label the nodes *N1, N2,* and *N3* as shown on the schematic.

Click Help in the menu for more information on creating the schematic.

6. Click on Simulate and then select the
   Edit Simulation Cmd in the menu. Select
   DC op pnt. Click on *OK*. A ".*op*"
   command will appear which can be
   placed anywhere on the schematic.

7. Click on *Simulate* and select *Run*. If
   there are no errors, you will see an
   "*Operating Point*" file.

   The Spice netlist shows the connections
   of the parts, part models, and types of
   analysis to be performed.

```
        --- Operating Point ---
    V(n1):        6               voltage
    V(n2):        4.18692         voltage
    V(n3):        4.07477         voltage
    I(R4):        1.86916e-006    device_current
    I(R3):        1.86916e-006    device_current
    I(R2):        0.0186916       device_current
    I(R1):        0.0186916       device_current
```

```
Netlist

R1  N1  N2  97
R2  N2  0  224
R3  N1  N3  1.03meg
R4  N3  0  2.18meg
V1  N1  0  6  Rser=0
.op
.backanno
.end
```

Exercise and Analysis

1. Simulate the loading effect of the voltmeter at nodes 2 and 3 using a resistor whose
   resistance is equal to the meter's internal resistance. Compare simulated results to
   your measured results in Experiment 4.

2. Simulate the loading effect of the ammeter using a resistor whose resistance is equal
   to the meter's internal resistance.   Compare simulated results to your measured
   results in Experiment 4.

Experiment 7: Kirchhoff's Voltage and Current Laws

Introduction

Kirchhoff's voltage and current laws are very important in circuit analysis. Kirchhoff's voltage law says that what goes up must come down. If you take any path around a circuit and return to where you started, all of the voltage drops in that path should equal all of the voltage rises. The algebraic sum of the voltages for any closed path must equal zero.

Kirchhoff's current law says that what goes in must come out. All of the currents entering a node must equal all of the currents leaving a node.

$$\text{KVL: } \sum_{i=1}^{n} V_i = 0 \qquad \text{KCL: } \sum_{i=1}^{n} I_i = 0$$

Objectives

In previous lab exercises we have made use of Kirchhoff's voltage law when we summed voltages in series circuits. This exercise will focus on using Kirchhoff's Voltage Law and Kirchhoff's current law in parallel and series-parallel circuits.

Procedure

Equipment and Parts
Power Supply, DMM, and Breadboard. Resistors: 100, 220, 330, and 470, all ¼ watt, 5%.

Part 1: Parallel Circuits

1. Measure and record the values of the resistors that you will use in the circuit.

    R1_____   R2_____   R3_____

2. Connect the circuit on the right so that it will be easy to insert the DMM in series with each component for measuring current. This circuit has three parallel branches. The voltage across each branch is exactly 4.0 volts.

    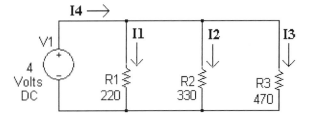

    Be very careful when switching the meter between measuring voltage and measuring current. Trying to measure voltage on the current range may cause damage to the meter, circuit, or the power supply.

DMM's usually have a fuse in their current measuring circuit. If your meter does not read current, it may be that the fuse needs replacement.

3.   Carefully measure and record the currents, I1, I2, I3, and I4. Use the 20 mA meter range. Note and record the meter's resistance, R_m, on the 20 mA range.

R$_m$ _____   (Refer to the instrument manual or ask the instructor.)

I1_____   I2 _____   I3 _____   I4 _____

4.   Prepare a spreadsheet for data entry as shown below. R4 will be used in part 2 of this exercise. Rows 11 through 15 of this spreadsheet will be used for part 2.

	A	B	C	D	E	F
1		R1	R2	R3	R4	
3	Measured R					
5	PART 1	I1	I2	I3	I4	
6	Measured I					
7	Calculated I					
8	% Error					

Part 2: Series-Parallel Circuits

1.   Use the same resistors for R1, R2, and R3 as you used in part 1. Measure and record the value of R4.

R4_____

Connect the circuit on the right. Set the source voltage to exactly 10.0 V.

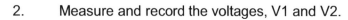

2.   Measure and record the voltages, V1 and V2.

V1_____   V2_____

3.   Currents: I1, I2, and I3 will be determined by using the voltage drop across the resistors and Ohm's Law.

$$I1 = \frac{10-V1}{R1} \qquad I2 = \frac{V1-V2}{R2} = \frac{V2}{R4} \qquad I3 = \frac{V1}{R3}$$

These equations may be entered into the spreadsheet cells E14, F14, and G14, using the appropriate cell references for the voltages and resistances. Refer to the analysis section for part 2.

Analysis, Part 1

1. Have the spreadsheet calculate the currents, I1, I2, and I3. Be sure to use the measured values of your resistors in the spreadsheet row 3. Also have the spreadsheet calculate the percent error in the measurements.

   For example, enter the equation: =4/B3 into cell B7, and: =100*(B6-B7)/B7 into cell B8.

2. Explain the most probable cause of the errors.

3. Show that Kirchhoff's Current Law holds (I1 = I2 + I3) exactly for the calculated currents, and approximately for the measured currents.

Analysis, Part 2

1. Calculate the voltages V1, and V2; record the results in the spreadsheet. Verify the calculations with an *OrCAD PSpice* simulation. Have the spreadsheet calculate the percent error for each measurement.

	A	B	C	D	E	F	G
11	PART 2	V1	V2		I1	I2	I3
13	Measured				X	X	X
14	Calculated						
15	% Error				X	X	X

2. Have the spreadsheet calculate the currents I1, I2, and I3 from the measured voltages, V1 and V2.

3. Show that the currents satisfy Kirchhoff's current law.

4. Explain why the measured results of part 2 are more accurate than the measured results of part 1.

5, Show that the voltages across R1, R2, and R4 add up to 10 V and satisfy Kirchhoff's voltage law.

Experiment 8: Potentiometer Voltage Dividers

Introduction

Potentiometers (pots) are very commonly used as variable voltage dividers. A potentiometer is basically a resistor with a sliding contact so that the resistance between the sliding contact and the ends of the potentiometer can be varied. Most pots are the single turn rotary type. Multi-turn rotary types and "slider" types are also available.

The schematic diagram of the potentiometer is shown below on the left in Figure a. Figure b shows how the rotary type operates, while Figure c shows how the slider type operates.

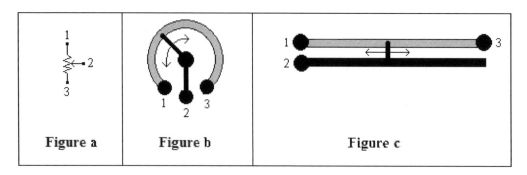

| Figure a | Figure b | Figure c |

Potentiometers are available in a wide range of resistance and power capabilities. The resistance rating is the total resistance (also the maximum resistance) of the potentiometer between terminals 1 and 3 as shown above. The slider moves between terminals 1 and 3. As the slider moves from terminal 1 toward terminal 3 the resistance between terminals 1 and 2 increases and between terminals 2 and 3 decreases. The resistance change may be proportional to the distance moved (linear taper pot) or may change logarithmically with the distance moved (audio/log taper pot).

Potentiometers may have a rotary shaft with a knob on it or they may have a screwdriver slot for screwdriver adjustment. The screwdriver types are usually called "trimmer pots" and are often used to calibrate "trim" circuits. The type used in this lab is a low power (1/4 or ½ watt) trimmer type.

Objectives

The purpose of this exercise is to become familiar with the potentiometer as a variable voltage divider. In addition, the voltage divider loading effect will be investigated.

Procedure

Equipment and Parts
Power Supply, DMM, and Breadboard. Resistors: 4.7k, and two 1k, ¼ watt, 5%. Trimmer Potentiometers: 100 Ω and 10 kΩ, ¼ or ½ watt.

Part 1: Basic Measurements

1.   Measure the values of R4 and R5.

     R4_____

     R5_____

2.   Neatly connect the circuit on the right. Include the "jumper" wires designated as JP1 through JP4 so that it will be easy to disconnect each potentiometer.

3.   Remove jumpers JP2 and JP4 so that the 1K load resistors are disconnected from the pots. Set the power supply voltage to exactly 3.00 V. Adjust each pot so that the voltage at each terminal 2 is exactly 1.50 V.

4.   Remove jumpers JP1 and JP3 so that the pots are disconnected from the power supply. Be careful to not disturb the pot settings. Measure and record the resistance of each pot from terminal 1 to ground, and from terminal 2 to ground. $R1_{13}$ is the resistance of R1 terminal 1 to ground, and $R1_{23}$ is the resistance of R1 terminal 2 to ground.

     $R1_{13}$ _____ $R1_{23}$ _____

     $R2_{13}$ _____ $R2_{23}$ _____

5.   Being careful not to disturb the pot settings, replace jumpers JP1 and JP3 so that the pots are connected to the power supply. Verify that the voltage on terminal 2 of each pot is still 1.50 V.

6.   Being careful not to disturb the pot settings, replace jumpers JP2 and JP4 so that terminal 2 of each pot is connected to a 1K load resistor. Make sure that the power supply voltage is still 3.00 V. Measure and record the voltage at terminal 2 of each pot with respect to ground. $V1_{23}$ is the voltage at terminal 2 of R1 to ground and $V2_{23}$ is the voltage at terminal 2 of R2 to ground.

     $V1_{23}$ _____ $V2_{23}$ _____

Part 2: Changing the Pot's Range of Adjustment

Suppose that it is desired to get a voltage variable from 1 V to 2 V by turning the pot from one end to the other using the 3.00 V power supply. Of course that voltage range is available from the circuit in part 1, but a 1 V change would correspond to rotating the pot over just one third of its range. We will investigate a circuit in this part of the exercise that will produce a 1 V to 2 V change over the pot's entire range.

1. Use the measured the values of the resistors, R1, R4 and R5 to be used in the circuit on the right. Measure the value of R7.

   R7_____

   Connect the circuit on the right. Set Vs to exactly 3.00 V.

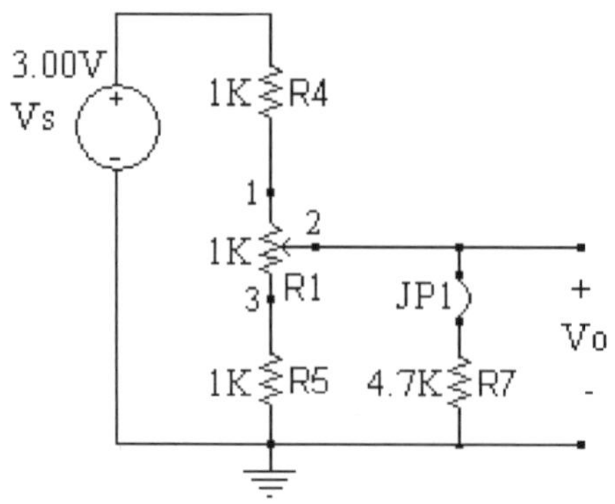

2. Disconnect the jumper, JP1. Measure and record the minimum and maximum value of the voltage Vo by turning the pot to both ends of its range.

   Vo(min)_____   Vo(max)_____

3. Connect the jumper, JP1, and measure and record the minimum and maximum value of the voltage Vo by turning the pot to both ends of its range.

   Vo(min)_____   Vo(max)_____

Analysis, Part 1

1. Use Ohm's law (voltage divider equation) and the measurements in part 1, step 4, to calculate the voltages $V1_{23}$ and $V2_{23}$. Comment on the accuracy of the measurements and the loading effect of the voltmeter.

2. Calculate the voltages $V1_{23}$ and $V2_{23}$ with the 1K resistors connected. Compare your results to the measurements in part 1, step 6. Calculate the percent error caused by the loading effect of the 1K resistors on the measurements. Which measurement had the greatest loading effect and why?

Analysis, Part 2

1. Calculate the theoretical values of Vo(min) and Vo(max) in part 2, step 2. Calculate the percent accuracy of these measurements.

2. Calculate the theoretical values of Vo(min) and Vo(max) in part 2, step 3. Calculate the percent accuracy of these measurements.

   Optional challenging problem:

   Note the effect of the 4.7K load resistance and redesign the circuit by changing the values of the fixed resistors in the voltage divider so that the voltage range is about 1 V to 2 V with the 4.7K load resistor connected.

Hint: Note that Vo1 must be 1 V in figure A and Vo 2 must be 2 V in figure B. You will need two simultaneous equations to solve for R1 and R2.

Use simulation to verify the results of step 3 above.

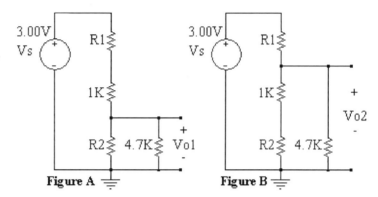

Figure A   Figure B

LTspice Simulation Example

A suggested circuit for analyzing this lab exercise is given below. The values of R1 and R4 should be the same, and the values of R3 and R6 should be the same. The values of R2 and R5 should be the measured value of the pot resistance, and R7 and R8 should have the measured value of the 4.7 KΩ resistor.

Try the calculated values for R1 and R3 below. Note that R1 = R4 and R3 = R8. Compare the resulting voltages at nodes N1 and N2 to those you calculated.

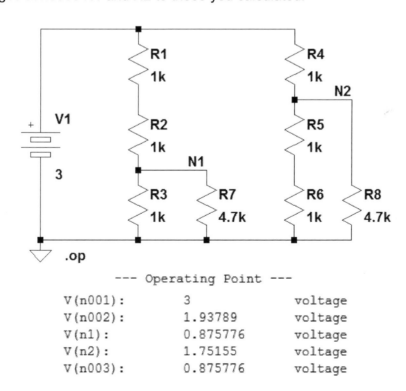

```
--- Operating Point ---
V(n001):        3               voltage
V(n002):        1.93789         voltage
V(n1):          0.875776        voltage
V(n2):          1.75155         voltage
V(n003):        0.875776        voltage
```

Operating point results above are for the resistor values in the circuit above.

29

Experiment 9: Mesh Current Analysis

Introduction

Mesh current analysis is based on Kirchhoff's voltage law: the algebraic sum of the voltages around any closed loop or path must be zero. The example circuit below has three meshes (closed loops).

$$V1 - I1\,R1 - (I1 - I2)\,R2 = 0$$

$$-(I2 - I1)\,R2 - I2\,R3 - (I2 - I3)\,R4 = 0$$

$$-(I3 - I2)\,R4 - I3\,R5 + V2 = 0$$

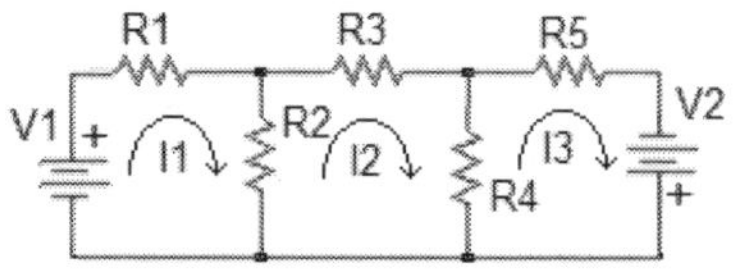

The application of Kirchhoff's voltage law results in the three independent simultaneous equations shown above. Refer to your textbook or instructor for more details, if needed.

The example above uses the three smallest meshes for the currents I1, I2, and I3. However, consider the circuit with a dependent current source shown below. The voltage across the current source is unknown. Kirchhoff's voltage law is applied to a larger loop, by-passing the current source. This is called the "super mesh". A second equation is obtained using the current source's dependency equation, as shown below.

$$V1 - I1\,R1 - I2\,R3 - I2\,R4 = 0 \quad \text{and given:} \quad Ix = 0.5 \cdot I2$$

Apply Kirchhoff's current law: $I1 - Ix - I2 = 0 \Rightarrow I1 = 1.5 \cdot I2$

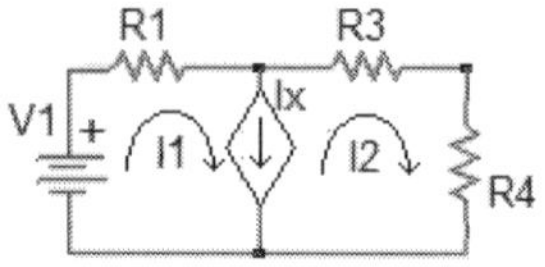

Objectives

The primary objective of this lab experiment is to gain experience in the application of mesh current analysis. Measurements will be made with the DMM and the results will be compared to theoretical calculations. In part 1 mesh analysis will be applied to a three-mesh resistor network. In part 2 super mesh analysis will be applied to a circuit with a dependent source.

Procedure

+--+
| Equipment and Parts |
| |
| DMM, Power Supply, and Breadboard. |
| Resistors: 470, 750, 1.2K, two 1.5K, ¼ watt, 5%. |
| Transistor: 2N3904. |
+--+

Part 1: Mesh Current Analysis – Resistor Network

1.   Measure the values of the resistors.

R_{470} _____ R_{750} _____ $R_{1.2k}$ _____

$R_{1.5k}$ _____ $R_{1.5k}$ _____

2. Connect the circuit on the right. Layout the circuit in the same form as the diagram. Do not use wires between the resistors.

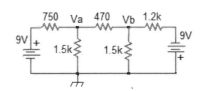

3. Set the plus and minus power supply voltages to exactly 9.0 V.

4. Measure and record the voltages Va and Vb.

Va _____   Vb _____

Part 2: Super Mesh Analysis – Dependent Current Source

1. Connect the circuit on the right. The transistor is a dependent current source. Its collector to emitter current is controlled by its base current, Ib.

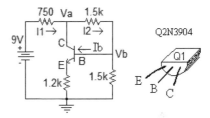

2. Measure and record the voltages Va and Vb.

Va _____   Vb _____

3. Measure and record the voltage at the emitter, V_E.

V_E _____

Analysis, Part 1

1. Use mesh analysis to solve the circuit from part 1 using your measured part values. Determine the net current in each of the 1.5 KΩ resistors and solve for the voltages Va and Vb.

2. Calculate the percent difference between the measured and calculated values.

Analysis, Part 2

1. The transistor and 1.2 KΩ resistor in the circuit can be replaced by a dependent current source whose current depends on the voltage Vb. Given that $V_E \cong Vb - 0.7$, write an equation for the current of the current source (Ix). The current Ib is negligible in this circuit and can be ignored.

2. The resulting circuit should look like the one on the right. Replace the 0.7 V in the equation for Ix in step 1 above with your measured value of V_{bE} ($V_{bE} = Vb - V_E$). Use your measured resistor values to calculate an accurate value of Ix.

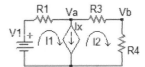

3. Use the value of Ix calculated in step 2 above and super mesh analysis to calculate the currents I1 and I2. Be sure to use your measured resistor values. Use your calculated currents, I1 and I2, to calculate the voltages, Va and Vb.

4. Calculate the percent difference between the calculated and measured voltages, Va and Vb.

31

Experiment 10: Node Voltage Analysis

Introduction

Node voltage analysis is based on Kirchhoff's current law: the algebraic sum of the currents at any node must be zero. The example circuit below has two essential nodes with the voltages Va and Vb.

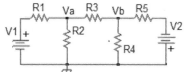

The application of Kirchhoff's voltage law results in the two independent simultaneous equations below. Refer to your textbook or instructor for more details, if needed.

$$\frac{Va-V1}{R1}+\frac{Va}{R2}+\frac{Va-Vb}{R3}=0 \quad and \quad \frac{Vb-Va}{R3}+\frac{Vb}{R4}+\frac{Vb-(-V2)}{R5}=0$$

In the example above the values of the voltage sources and the resistances are all assumed to be known. The number of equations equals the number of unknowns.

In the example below a red light emitting diode (LED) is connected between two nodes. The voltage across an LED varies with the current through it. A typical red LED may have about 1.7 V across it when its current is 5 mA, and 2.0 V across it when its current is increased to 20 mA.

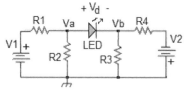

This circuit will be used as an example of the super node method. The nodes at Va and Vb will be taken as a super node. The super node equation sums the current away from each node as shown below. The second equation relates the LED voltage to Va and Vb.

$$\frac{Va-V1}{R1}+\frac{Va}{R2}+\frac{Vb}{R3}+\frac{Vb-V2}{R4}=0 \quad and \quad Va=Vb+V_d$$

The diode voltage, V_d, is actually a logarithmic function of the diode current. However, for the purpose of this experiment, we will measure V_d and use the measured value to calculate Va and Vb using the super node method.

Objectives

The primary objective of this lab experiment is to gain experience in the application of node voltage analysis. Measurements will be made with the DMM and the results will be compared to theoretical calculations. In part 1 node analysis will be applied to a resistor network. In part 2 super node analysis will be applied to a circuit with a dependent source.

Procedure

Equipment and Parts

DMM, Power Supply, and Breadboard.
Resistors: 470, 750, 1.2K, two 1.5K, all ¼ watt, 5%.
LED: Red (other colors may be used).

Part 1: Node Voltage Analysis – Resistor Network

1. Measure the values of the resistors.

   R_{470} _____ R_{750} _____ $R_{1.2k}$ _____

   $R_{1.5k}$ _____ $R_{1.5k}$ _____

2. Connect the circuit on the right. Layout the circuit in the same form as the diagram. Do not use wires between the resistors.

3. Set the plus and minus power supply voltages to exactly 9.0 volts.

4. Measure and record the voltages Va and Vb.

   Va _____ Vb _____

Part 2: Super Node Analysis – Dependent Voltage Source

1. Connect the circuit on the right. The LED may have one lead longer than the other. The longer lead is usually the one that goes to the positive voltage (the diodes anode).

2. Measure and record the voltages Va and Vb.

   Va _____ Vb _____

3. Calculate and record the voltage V_d, as $V_d = Va - Vb$.

   V_d _____

Analysis, Part 1

1. Use node voltage analysis to solve the circuit in part 1 for voltages Va and Vb. Use your measured part values to do the calculation.

2. Calculate the percent difference between the measured and calculated values of Va and Vb.

33

Analysis, Part 2

1. Use the super node method to solve for the voltages Va and Vb using your measured part values.

    First write the equations summing currents away from the Va and Vb voltage nodes, ignoring the LED current.

    Next write an equation relating the voltages Va and Vb to the measured value of the LED voltage (refer to the introduction to this experiment).

    Solve the equations simultaneously for Va and Vb.

2. Calculate the percent difference between the calculated and measured voltages, Va and Vb.

3. Simulate your circuit using your part values. Use a voltage source (VDC) in place of the LED and set its value to the voltage that you measured across your LED.

Example PSpice Simulation

Since an LED is not available in the evaluation version of PSpice, an ordinary diode was used in the example circuit below. For the simulation in analysis step 3, you need to replace the diode with a voltage source and set its value to the desired LED voltage.

Calculate the voltages in the PSpice example below using the super node method and the displayed voltage drop across the diode (1.916 – 0.9088).

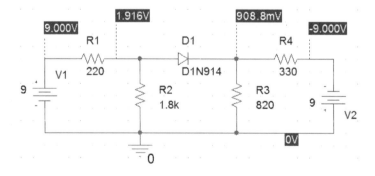

Experiment 11: Thevenin's Theorem and the Bridge Circuit

Introduction

Thevenin's theorem states that a circuit between two nodes, a and b, can be replaced by a single voltage source (Thevenin voltage, V_{TH}) in series with a single resistance (Thevenin resistance, R_{TH}). The Thevenin voltage is equal to the "open circuit" voltage between nodes a and b. The Thevenin resistance is equal to the resistance between nodes a and b.

Norton's theorem states that a circuit between two nodes, a and b, can be replaced by a single current source (Norton current, I_N) in parallel with a single resistance (Norton resistance, R_N). The Norton current is equal to the "short circuit" current between nodes a and b. The Norton resistance is equal to the resistance between nodes a and b.

The application of Thevenin's or Norton's theorem may also require the application of other analysis methods. Determining an "open circuit" voltage or a "short circuit" current may require the use of node voltage or mesh current analysis. Having a Thevenin or Norton equivalent circuit as a model of a more complex circuit makes it much easier to determine how the circuit will perform when loads or sources are connected to it.

It is possible to find the Thevenin or Norton equivalent of a circuit by measurement, without knowing, necessarily, the components and connections of the original circuit. If we can measure the original circuit's open circuit voltage and short circuit current, we can then determine the circuit's Thevenin or Norton resistance: $R_{Th} = R_N = \dfrac{V_{Th}}{I_N}$.

Wheatstone Bridge

Wheatstone bridge circuits are used in many applications in electronics. A common problem is to find the voltage across the center element (R5 on the right) and the current through it. The node voltage method can be used to find the voltage. However, if the value of the center element is varied, it is easier to use the Thevenin equivalent circuit.

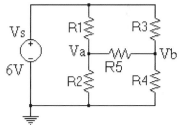

The Thevenin voltage of the circuit above "external" to R5 is found by determining the open circuit voltage, Va – Vb, with R5 removed.

The Thevenin resistance is found by determining the resistance across the terminals where R5 was removed, with the resistance of Vs equal to zero.

When R5 is removed, Va and Vb can be calculated with the voltage divider equation.

$$Va = \frac{R2}{R1+R2} Vs \quad \text{and} \quad Vb = \frac{R4}{R3+R4} Vs$$

The Thevenin voltage can be calculated as $V_{Th} = Va - Vb$.

It can be shown that the Thevenin resistance is:

$$R_{Th} = (R1 \| R2) + (R3 \| R4) = \frac{R1 \cdot R2}{R1 + R2} + \frac{R3 \cdot R4}{R3 + R4}$$

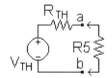

According to Thevenin's Theorem, the Thevenin equivalent circuit on the right will produce the same voltage across R5, for any value of R5, as the original bridge circuit.

Objectives

A comparison will be made between the solutions for the voltage across the resistor, R5, using the node voltage method and the Thevenin equivalent circuit method. The Thevenin equivalent circuit will be determined by measurement as well as by calculation. The value of the center element, R5, will be varied in both circuits to show that they are equivalent. The Thevenin equivalent circuit will also demonstrate the Maximum Power Transfer Theorem.

Procedure

Equipment and Parts

Power Supply, DMM, and Breadboard.
R1 = 1500   R2 = 2200   R3 = 1000   R4 = 470
R5 values: 390, 680, 1200, 2200, 3900.

1. Measure and record the values of all the resistors you will be using. 1000

    1500

    R1 __1472__   R2 _____   R3 ___985___

    R4 _____   R5_390 _____   R5_680 _____

    R5_1200 __1180__   R5_2200 _____   R5_3900 __3886__

2. Set the DMM to read DC volts. Use the meter range which gives you at least three significant digits. Connect the circuit in figure A below. Use R5 = 390-ohms initially.

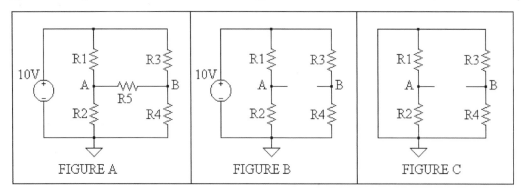

3. Set the power supply voltage to 10.0 V.

36

4.   Measure and record the voltage V_{AB} in the table on the right for the given values of R5.

R5 (labeled)	Vab
390	
680	
1200	
2200	
3900	
∞ (open)	

5.   Turn off the power supply and disconnect it from the circuit. Then connect a wire from the top of R1 to the bottom of R2, as shown in Figure C.

Use the ohmmeter to measure the resistance of the circuit between nodes A and B.   This resistance is the measured Thevenin resistance.

6.   Record the Thevenin resistance, R_{TH}, from step 5 above. Record the voltage Vab with R5 = ∞ from step 4 as the Thevenin voltage, V_{TH}.

7. R_{TH} _____ V_{TH} _____

8.   Use the values in step 7 above to connect a Thevenin equivalent of the bridge circuit for nodes A and B. Use a combination of resistors for R_{TH} to match the resistance recorded in step 7 to within one percent.

The exact value may be obtained by connecting your bridge circuit resistors as shown below.

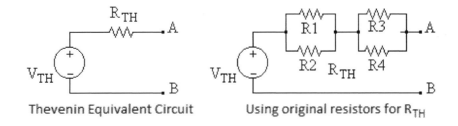

Thevenin Equivalent Circuit   Using original resistors for R_{TH}

9.   Set the power supply voltage to V_{TH}.   Measure and record the voltage V_{AB} in the Thevenin equivalent circuit for the given values of R5.

R5	Vab
390	
680	
1200	
2200	
3900	

Analysis

1. Enter the data for the voltage V_{AB} into a spreadsheet as shown below:

	A	B	C	D	E
1	R5 (measured)	Vab (Step 4)	Vab (Step 9)	% Error	Power (Step 9)
2	390				
3	680				
4	1200				
5	2200				
6	3900				
7	∞ Open				

2. Use the measured values of R5 in column A. Use the equation for percent error in cell D2, and use "fill down" to have the spreadsheet calculate the error for cells D2 to D7.

    Similarly, enter the equation for power in cell E2 and use "fill down".
    % Error = ((2 - B2) / B2) *100   Power = C2*C2 / A2

3. Solve the circuit in Figure A for the voltage V_{AB}, for R5 equal to 1200-ohms, using the node voltage method.

4. Simulate the circuit in Figure A. Generate a list of values of Vab for all 5 of your measured values for R5. Use the spreadsheet to calculate the percent error between the simulated and measured results (measured values from step 5).

PSpice Example: Simulating a Bridge Circuit and Variable Resistor

In the circuit simulation below, the value of R5 was varied. Note that its value is indicated as "{RX}". Two methods of analysis will be used.

First the circuit will be simulated for 5 specific values of R5. Simulation output will be a list of voltages across R5, and a list of currents through R5, for each specific value of R5.

Second the circuit will be simulated by increasing the value of R5 from 100 Ω to 5000 Ω in 10 Ω steps. The output will be a graph generated by the "*Probe*" feature of *PSpice*.

Get the Parts

Get and place the resistors. Get the voltage source, *Vdc*. Set the voltage to 10 V. Get the printer, *VPRINT2*, and connect it across R5 as shown.

Get the part, *PARAM* . Place it in any convenient place. Get and place the analog ground (0/SOURCE).

Note: *VPRINT2*, and *PARAM*, are in the "*Special*" library.

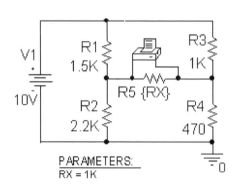

38

Setup the Analysis

Double click on the printer, VPRINT2, select "DC" and type "ok" for value.

Save and exit.   Note that *"Filter by: OrCAD-PSpice"* is selected.

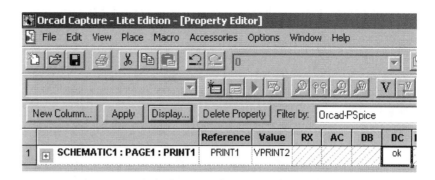

Double click on *"PARAMETERS"* on the diagram. Set RX = 1K.

If the column "RX" does not appear, click on *New Column* and add it.

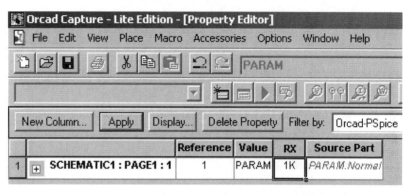

Click on *PSpice* in the menu bar. Select *New Simulation Profile*.

Name the profile in the dialog box that follows, such as: "R5 DC Sweep".

Set up the simulation as shown in the dialog box on the right.

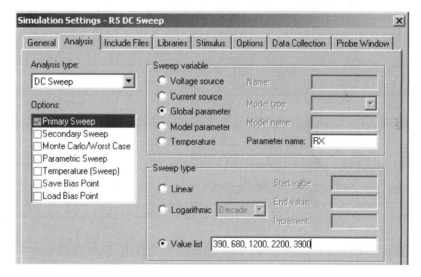

Simulate the Circuit

After the simulation runs, a *"Probe"* window opens without traces on it. Click on *View* in the menu and select *Output File*.

Scroll down to the "DC TRANSFER CURVES" and note the results. You can copy the results into another file, such as a word processor.

In addition to the simulation results, the output file contains the circuit's "netlist". The netlist specifies the parts, their values, and the nodes to which they are connected. It includes analysis information and part models.

To save paper, print only the necessary simulation results. These can be copied to a word processor document and edited. Simulation results output file on the right:

RX	V(N00297,N00239)
3.900E+02	6.693E-01
6.800E+02	9.881E-01
1.200E+03	1.368E+00
2.200E+03	1.772E+00
3.900E+03	2.097E+00

Graphical output with "Probe"

The printer was deleted in the circuit on the right. Nodes "A" and "B" were added using the "N!" button in the vertical menu bar.

"Markers" were added by clicking on PSpice in the main menu and selecting *Markers* followed by *Voltage Differential*. Place the first marker at node A and the second at node B. Short cut commands are also available.

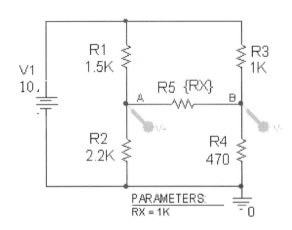

The value of the resistor, R5, is varied from 100 Ω to 5000 Ω in steps of 10 Ω. Set up new simulation settings as follows:

Set "*Analysis type*" to *DC SWEEP*, and set the following:

Sweep Variable = Global Parameter,   *Sweep Type* = Linear
Name = RX,   *Start Value* = 100,   *End Value* = 5000,   *Increment* = 10

Simulate the Circuit: The probe window will open with a graph of V(A,B), the voltage at node A with respect to node B, as a function of the value of R5.

The top graph on the right is a plot of the power dissipation of R5. In the "*Probe Window*" menu, click on Plot and select *Add Plot to Window*. Then click on *Add Trace* and in the "*Trace Expression*" box, type: V(A,B)*V(A,B)/RX.

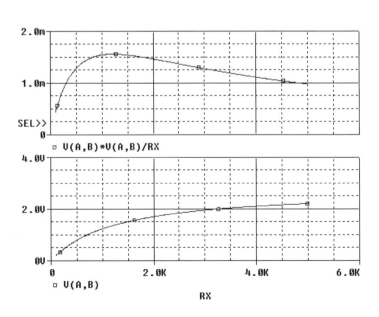

A cursor can be used to display the X and Y values on the graph. Click on `Trace` in the probe window menu bar, then on *Cursor*, then on *Display*. Clicking a mouse button on the symbol of a trace at the bottom of the graph will cause that mouse button to move the cursor over that trace and display the X and Y values in the "Cursor" window.

LTspice Simulation of a Bridge Circuit and Variable Resistor

In the circuit simulation below, the value of R5 was varied from 100 Ω to 4000 Ω in 100 steps. R5's value is indicated as "{RX}" on the schematic.

Get the Parts

Get and place the resistors. Get and place the voltage source and ground. Connect the circuit. Label nodes N1, N2, and N3.

Setup the Analysis

Spice directives can be entered directly into the schematic by pressing the letter "s". Enter the directives ".*op*" and ".*step param RX 100 4000 100*" and place them in a convenient place on the schematic. Value of R5 is varied from 100 Ω to 4000 Ω in 100 Ω steps.

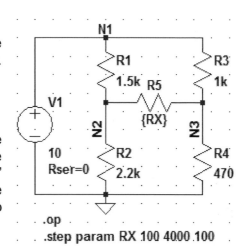

Simulate the Circuit

Move the mouse to N2, left click and drag the probe to N3. This will display the voltage across R5. To plot of the power dissipation of R5, click in the plot window, click on *Plot Settings* in the main menu, select *Add trace*, type V(n2,n3)*-I(R5), and click *ok*.

The plot on the right shows that maximum power occurs for a value of R5 of about 1200 ohms.

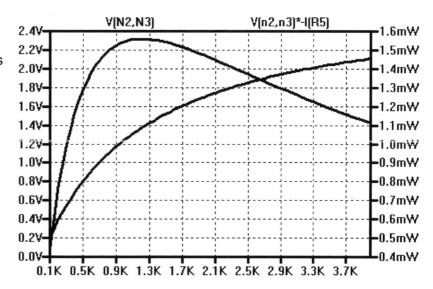

41

Experiment 12: Transistor / Dependent Current Source

Introduction

One of the greatest inventions of the 20th century is the transistor. It has allowed the miniaturization of electronic circuits by making possible the integrated circuit or IC. It has revolutionized computers, and prompted many other technological advances.

In this experiment you will see how the transistor acts as a current controlled current source and how it can be modeled that way. The transistor used in this lab has three terminals that are called the emitter, collector, and base. The property of the transistor that makes it so important is that a small current flowing into the base can control a much larger current flow between the emitter and collector.

The relationship between the base current and the emitter to collector current is called the transistor's "current amplification factor", beta (β). β is typically between 100 and 300.

A schematic symbol, circuit model, and PSpice model of the transistor are shown on the right.

$Ic = \beta \cdot Ib$

$Ie = Ic + Ib$

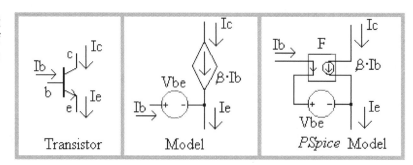

Ib is the base current, Ic the collector current, and Ie is the emitter current. Note that the equation, $Ie = Ic + Ib$, is an expression of Kirchhoff's current law.

A voltage source, Vbe, is added to the models to simulate the voltage between the transistor's base and emitter, which is typically between 0.65 V and 0.75 V.

Objectives

A simple transistor circuit will be evaluated as a current controlled current source and as a constant current source. The transistor's current gain, β, will be measured. This parameter will be used in the dependent current source model in *PSpice*. The current control ability of the transistor will be measured and compared to *PSpice* or *LTspice* simulation.

Procedure

Equipment and Parts
DMM, Power Supply (15 V and 0 to 6 V), and Breadboard. Transistor: 2N3904 or 2N2222. Resistors: 100, 470, 1K, 2.2K, 4.7K, 6.8K, 8.2K, 10K, 22K, 100K, all ¼ watt, 5%.

Part 1: Dependent Current Source

Measure the values of your resistors.

Labeled Value	Measured Value	Labeled Value	Measured Value
100		6.8K	
470		8.2K	
1K		10K	
2.2K		22K	
4.7K		100K	

1. Connect circuit on the right. Q1 is the transistor. Note that Q1's emitter lead is on the left when the transistor's flat side is facing you. Set V1 to 0 V and V2 to 15.0V.

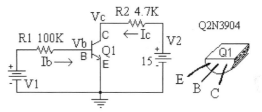

2. Connect the DMM to measure Vc. Adjust V1 to get the following voltages for Vc: 1, 2, 3, 4, 5, 6, 7, 8, 9, 10, 11, 12, 13, and 14 V. For each value of Vc, measure and record V1 and Vb. Set up a spreadsheet table as shown on the right to record the voltages.

	A	B	C	D	E	F
1	Vc	V1	Vb	Ib	Ic	β
3	1					
4	2					
5	3					
6	4					
7	5					
8	6					
9	7					
10	8					
11	9					
12	10					
13	11					
14	12					
15	13					
16	14					

3. Copy your results into a spreadsheet and have the spreadsheet calculate Ib, Ic, and β for each value of Vc. See format on the right.

$$Ib = (V1 - Vb) / 100000 \qquad Ic = (15 - Vc) / (4700) \qquad β = Ic / Ib.$$

Part 2: Constant Current Source

1. Make sure V2 is still exactly 15.0 V and adjust V1 so that Vc is exactly 7.0 V, as shown on the right. Change R2 to the following values: 100, 470, 1K, 2.2K, 6.8K, 8.2K, 10K, 22K, and record Vc for each value.

2. Copy your results into a spreadsheet and have the spreadsheet calculate Ic for each value of Vc. See format on the right. $Ic = (15 - Vc) / R2$.

	A	B	C
1	R2	Vc	Ic
3	100		
4	470		
5	1000		
6	2200		
7	4700	7.0	
8	6800		
9	8200		
10	10000		
11	22000		

Analysis, Part 1

1. Use the spreadsheet from part 1 to plot the collector current, Ic, of the transistor as a function of its base current, Ib (Ic on the vertical axis).

2. Simulate the circuit from part 1. Use a current controlled current source to show that the transistor acts as a current controlled current source by plotting the current of the current source as a function of its controlling current.

   Set the gain of the current source to the average value of β (obtained by averaging the β results for Vc values of 4, 5, 6, 7, 8, 9, and 10 volts). See example below.

3. Compare your spreadsheet plot to your simulation plot. Over what range of Ic do the plots approximately match? Over what range of Ic do they not match?

Analysis, Part 2

1. Use the spreadsheet from part 2 to plot the collector current, Ic, of the transistor as a function of R2 (with Ic on the vertical axis).

2. Simulate the circuit from part 2. Refer to the example simulation on the next page. Use a current controlled current source for the transistor to show that it does act as a constant current source.

   Compare measured results to *PSpice* results. Where does the transistor fail as a constant current source?

   a) Use your measured resistor values and average value of β (from step 2 of the analysis of part 1) for the gain of the current controlled current source.

   b) Use "DC sweep" to obtain value of Ic for each value of R2.

Example PSpice simulation of Part 1

Circuit Diagram

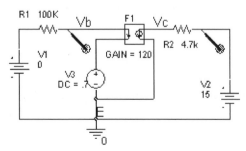

Simulation Results

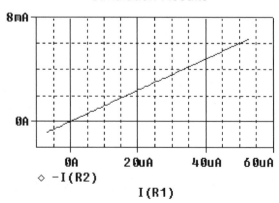

Enter the schematic diagram shown above. The current controlled current source, F1, is in the library: Analog.olb.

44

The horizontal axis of the simulation plot was changed to "I(R1)" by clicking Plot in the probe menu and selecting *Axis Settings / X Axis / Axis Variable*.

Double click the left mouse button on F1 and set the gain value to the value of your transistor's beta in the property editor. In this example, GAIN = 120.

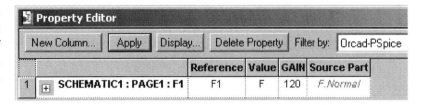

V1 and V2 are "VDC" in the source library. V3 is "VSRC" in the source library. The source, V3, represents the base to emitter voltage of the transistor (Vbe). In this example, V1 = 0 V and V3 = 0.7 V. V1 will be "swept from 0 to 6 V in the simulation.

Set the analysis to "DC Sweep". Select the voltage source, V1, and set the sweep to "linear" from 0 to 6 V in increments of 0.1 V. Simulate the circuit. The plot shows I(R2), which represents Ic as a function of I(R1), which represents Ib (after changing the X axis variable to I(R1)).

Example PSpice simulation of Part 2

Connect the circuit on the right.

Be sure that the gain for F1 is the same as in part 1. The printer at node "Vc" is the part "VPRINT1" from the "Special" library.

Current Ic is measured by the part "IPRINT" from the "Special" library.

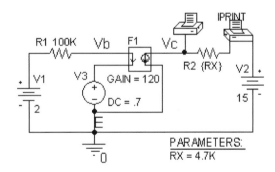

Double click on each printer. Type "ok" under "DC" in the property editor dialog box.

Set V1 to the value that resulted in Vc = 7 V in part 1. Your value of V1 will depend on β.

Change the value of R2 to "{RX}". Include the curly brackets. Get the part "PARAM" from the "Special" library.

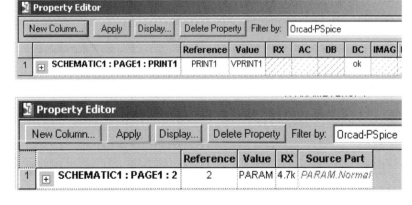

Double click on "PARAMETERS:" in your diagram to open its property editor.

If the column "RX" does not appear in the property editor, click on "New Column" and add the column "RX". Select that column by clicking on it, enter the default value of RX (the measured value of your 4.7K resistor).

Click on *Display* and set the display to *Name and Value*. When you leave the property editor you should see the name and value displayed on your diagram.

Set the analysis to "DC Sweep", and "Sweep variable" to "Global Parameter". Set the parameter name to "RX" and the "Sweep type" to "Value list". Type the values of your resistors in ascending order separated by commas.

Simulate the circuit. When a blank graph appears, click on View and select *Output file*. You will see a "net list" showing the parts, values, connections, and models. Scroll down to the "DC Transfer Curves" to see your results. You can copy any part of the output and paste it into a word processor document. If you print the output, to save paper, select only the data you need. See edited results below:

DC TRANSFER CURVES   TEMPERATURE =   27.000 DEG C

RX	V(VC)	RX	I(V_PRINT2)
1.000E+02	1.484E+01	1.000E+02	1.560E-03
4.700E+02	1.427E+01	4.700E+02	1.560E-03
1.000E+03	1.344E+01	1.000E+03	1.560E-03
2.200E+03	1.157E+01	2.200E+03	1.560E-03
4.700E+03	7.668E+00	4.700E+03	1.560E-03
6.800E+03	4.392E+00	6.800E+03	1.560E-03
8.200E+03	2.208E+00	8.200E+03	1.560E-03
1.000E+04	-6.000E-01	1.000E+04	1.560E-03
2.200E+04	-1.932E+01	2.200E+04	1.560E-03

The transistor has the following limitations when compared to the controlled current source model:

a)   The base to emitter voltage, Vbe, must be greater than about 0.6 V before current will flow into the base.

b)   The gain parameter of the transistor, β, is not constant over the transistor's entire operating range.

c)   The maximum current, Ic, through the transistor is limited by the value of the power supply voltage and the value of the resistors in the transistor's collector and emitter circuits.

Example LTspice simulation of Part 1

Connect the circuit as shown on the right.   The current controlled current source, F1, is given the value "*V1 120*".   This makes F1's current equal to the current through V1 times 120.

Set the simulation to "DC Sweep" and to sweep V2 from 0 to 6 V in 0.1 V steps.

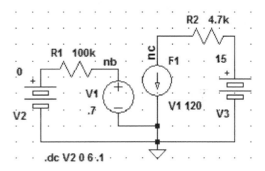

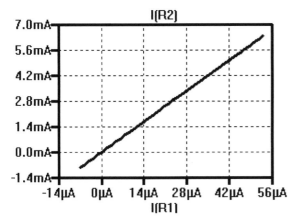

The vertical axis of the plot is the current through R2, which represents the transistor's collector current, Ic.

The horizontal axis of the plot is the current through R1, which represents the transistor's base current, Ib, in this model

Set the gain of the current source, F1, to that of your transistor to compare your measured results to the simulation.

To generate the plot above, the horizontal axis variable was changed from V(V2) to I(R1) by clicking just below the horizontal axis.   This opens the horizontal axis dialog box .

Change the "Quantity Plotted" to I(R1). This generates a plot of I(R2) as a function of the current through R1.

Experiment 13: Op-Amp / Controlled Voltage Source

Introduction

Ideal operational amplifier approximation assumes that op-amp input currents are negligible and can be ignored. The op-amp's input resistance is assumed to be infinite and its output resistance is assumed to be zero. The op-amp can be modeled as a voltage controlled voltage source whose output voltage is controlled by its input voltage.

Refer to the model diagram on the right. A typical (data book) value for an op-amp's input resistance is 2 megohms and output resistance is 75 ohms. When the op-amp is used in a circuit with negative feedback, the effective input resistance increases and output resistance decreases.

Objectives

This experiment will demonstrate that the operational amplifier acts as a voltage controlled voltage source. Also the validity of the ideal op-amp approximations will be investigated. The op-amp's input currents and voltages will be measured.

Procedure

Equipment and Parts
Power Supply: +15, -15, and +5 V, DMM, Breadboard. Op-amp: μA741. Resistors: 10K, two 100K and two 150K, all ¼ watt, 5%.

Part 1: Input Currents

1.   Measure and record the values of your resistors.

Labeled Value	Measured Value	Labeled Value	Measured Value
100k(1)		100k(2)	
10k		150k	

2.   Connect the circuit below. Refer to the top view of the op-amp for pin numbering.

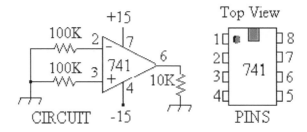

3. Carefully measure and record the voltages at pin 2 and pin 3 of the op-amp. Refer to the picture on the right. Note the dual polarity power supply connections, +15V and -15V, both referenced to ground.

V₂ _____

V₃ _____

Part 2: Controlled Voltage Source

1. Connect the circuit in Figure A below:

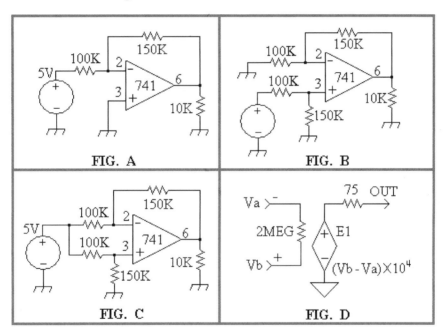

2. Note that although the +15 V and -15 V supplies are not shown on the diagrams, however, the op-amp must have these voltages to operate.

3. For the circuit in Figure A, measure and record the voltages on pins 2, 3, and 6 of the op-amp.

    V₂ _____   V₃ _____   V₆ _____

4. Connect the circuit in Figure B. Measure and record the voltages on pins 2, 3, and 6 of the op-amp.

    V₂ _____   V₃ _____   V₆ _____

5.   Connect the circuit in Figure C. Measure and record the voltages on pins 2, 3, and 6 of the op-amp.

V_2 _____ V_3 _____ V_6 _____

Analysis

1.   Use the pin 2 to ground and the pin 3 to ground voltages from part 1, step 3, to calculate the currents into pins 2 and 3. Indicate the current's direction using positive for current into the pin, and negative for current out of the pin.

   You should convince yourself that these currents are very small, and that they can indeed be ignored when using the node voltage method to analyze the circuit.

2.   Use the node voltage method to calculate the output voltage of the circuit in Figure C. Show that the output voltage of the circuit in Figure C can be calculated using the superposition principle. The output of the circuit in Figure C can be obtained as the superposition of the outputs of the circuits in Figures A and B.

3.   Figure D is a simple voltage controlled voltage source model of the op-amp. Use this model and the node voltage method to calculate the output voltage in Figure C.

4.   Use the model in Figure D to simulate the circuit in Figure C. Compare the simulation to your measurements.

PSpice Voltage Controlled Voltage Source Simulation

An op-amp is an example of a device which can be modeled by a voltage controlled voltage source. The *PSpice* part name for this source is "*E*" and it is found in the "*analog*" library.

The diagrams below show how an op-amp is modeled.   Rin is the op-amp's nominal input resistance and Ro is the op-amp's nominal output resistance. Values for these can be found in an op-amp data book.   Typically Rin is about 2 megohms and Ro is about 75 ohms.   The gain of the part "*E*" is set by double clicking on it. A value of 10,000 is typical for an op-amp.

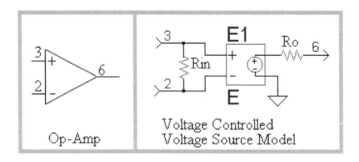

Example Circuit

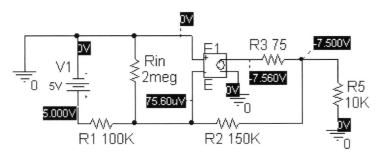

V1 was set to 5 volts. Part "*E*" is in the "*Analog*" library. Its gain was set to 10,000. The simulation type was set to "*Bias Point*". The "*V*" button was enabled in the main menu to display the voltages directly on the schematic diagram. The simulation must be run before the voltages appear.

Example: LTspice Voltage Controlled Voltage Source Simulation

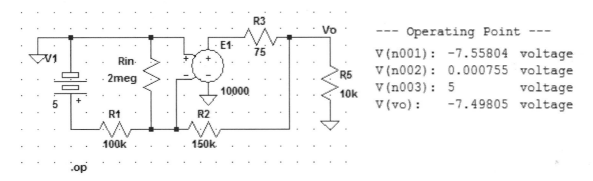

```
--- Operating Point ---
V(n001):  -7.55804   voltage
V(n002):  0.000755   voltage
V(n003):  5          voltage
V(vo):    -7.49805   voltage
```

Example: OrCAD PSpice Analog Behavior Model (ABM) Simulation

PSpice is able to perform math operations using the parts in the ABM library. This example uses the parts "DIFF" and "GAIN" to model a non-inverting op-amp. V1 was swept from -100 mV to +100 mV.

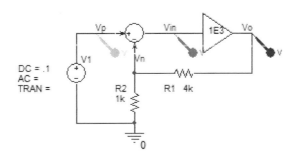

Compare the graph below on the left where the gain was set to 1000, to the one on the right, where the gain was set to 10.

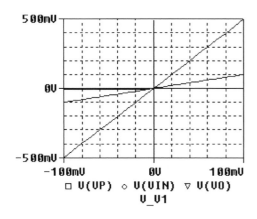
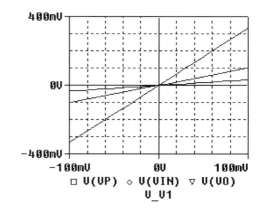

Model equations: $Vin = Vp - Vn$ $Vo = A \cdot Vin = A \cdot (Vp - Vn)$ $Vn = \dfrac{R2}{R2 + R1} Vo = B \cdot Vo$

$$Vo = \frac{A}{1 + A \cdot B} Vp = \frac{1}{\frac{1}{A} + B} Vp \Rightarrow if\ A \rangle\rangle Vp,\ then\ Vo = \frac{1}{B} Vp = (1 + \frac{R1}{R2}) Vp$$

Note that if A>>1, then the gain of the circuit is that of an ideal op-amp.

Experiment 14: Function Generator and Oscilloscope

Introduction

A *function generator* is an instrument that produces a variety of waveforms whose amplitudes and frequencies can be varied. Typically, a function generator produces sine, square, and triangular waveforms. Frequencies may range from less than 1 Hz to over 1 MHz. The amplitude can usually be varied from close to zero to about 20 V peak-to-peak

An *oscilloscope* is an instrument used mainly to observe waveforms in the time domain. In the YT mode, it produces a graph of voltage versus time. An oscilloscope may also be operated in the XY mode, where the voltage on the vertical axis is be plotted against the voltage on the horizontal axis.

Most oscilloscopes have two inputs which can be displayed simultaneously. The vertical axis is calibrated in volts per division, and the horizontal axis is calibrated in seconds per division (in the XY mode, the horizontal axis is also calibrated in volts per division). Voltages or signals are amplified and scaled by "vertical amplifiers". A "time base" circuit scales the horizontal axis. A "trigger" circuit is used to obtain a stable display.

The main purpose of this lab is to learn how to use the function generator and oscilloscope. A *frequency counter* may be used to measure the frequency of the function generator. However, some function generators will display their exact frequency, so a frequency counter may not be needed.

The Oscilloscope

Modern oscilloscopes digitize the signals input to the vertical amplifiers, store the digitized signals in memory, process the information stored in memory, and display the results on an LCD screen. Digitizing is done by an "analog to digital converter". The vertical signal is sampled and converted to a sequence of binary words. For example, the Tektronix TDS1002 oscilloscope converts the input signal to a series of 8 bit "bytes" and stores 2500 bytes in memory as data. This data memory is processed and displayed on its LCD screen.

Most oscilloscopes have a variety of modes of operation. In the time mode (YT), the horizontal time scale is set by a *TIME/DIV* control. The vertical scale is set by the *VOLTS/DIV* controls. In the XY mode the horizontal scale is set by a *VOLTS/DIV* control. In the MATH mode signals from the vertical channels may be added, subtracted, or converted to another format.

A "trigger" circuit is used to obtain a stable display. If the waveform being displayed is periodic, each successive sweep can be made to coincide on the left side of the screen by using the trigger (*TRIG*) controls. The beginning of each sweep is delayed until the waveform reaches the exact same position in the cycle so that each sweep produces an identical picture. If the waveform is not triggered properly, the display is unsynchronized and unstable. You must select the proper trigger source to match the waveform being displayed, and you can adjust the trigger *LEVEL* and *SLOPE* to begin the waveform where desired.

Simplified Block Diagram of a Digital Oscilloscope

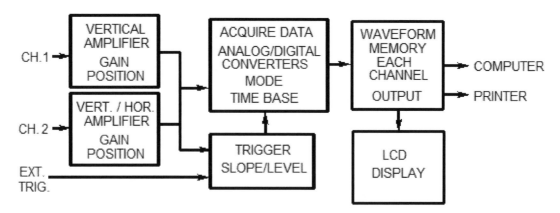

The block diagram above shows the functional blocks of a typical digital oscilloscope. One needs to understand the function of each block and the signal paths in the diagram to be able to use the oscilloscope effectively.

Each vertical channel has three basic controls: *VOLTS/DIV, VERTICAL POSITION,* and *INPUT COUPLING.* In XY mode, channel 2 becomes a horizontal amplifier.

A *VOLTS/DIV* control scales the display by setting the gain of the vertical / horizontal amplifier. The vertical axis of the oscilloscope usually has 8 major divisions. For example, the Tektronix TDS1002 vertical amplifier gain can be set from 2 millivolts per division to 5 volts per division.

A *VERTICAL POSITION* control positions the displayed signal vertically.

An *INPUT COUPLING* control sets the vertical input to AC, DC, or GND. In the AC mode, only AC signals are displayed. In the DC mode, both AC and DC signals are displayed. Selecting GND connects the input to ground so that no signal is displayed.

The *TIME BASE* sets the calibration of the horizontal axis. The horizontal axis of the oscilloscope usually has 10 major divisions. For example, the Tektronix TDS1002 time base can be set from 5 nanoseconds per division to 50 seconds per division. The display position can also be adjusted horizontally.

The *TRIGGER* circuit is used to get a stable display. The trigger source may be a signal from channel 1, channel 2, or an external source. The trigger point on the waveform is adjustable with the *LEVEL* and *SLOPE* controls. The trigger source may also be filtered.

Digital oscilloscopes usually have a means of connecting to a computer through a USB, GPIB, ethernet, or serial port. Data from the oscilloscope can be downloaded to the computer directly into spreadsheet programs.

Also the oscilloscope screen can be captured and copied to the computer's clipboard, or sent directly to a printer. The specific data acquisition capability depends on the oscilloscope and available software.

Note: The instructor may supplement this lab exercise with specific information on the types and models of instruments at your lab station.

Function Generator

The function generator typically generates sine waves, square waves, and triangle waves. The frequency and amplitude of these waves can be adjusted, and a "DC offset" can be added. The generator may have more than one output. The main output should go to your circuit. Another output may be provided which can be used to connect it to an oscilloscope trigger circuit or to a frequency counter.

Quality laboratory function generators use digital waveform synthesis to generate the output waveforms. Older analog function generators may not have an accurate frequency display so a frequency counter would be needed to set the frequency accurately.

Depending on the particular function generator, the frequency may be set using a *RANGE* switch and a variable *FREQUENCY* control, or by entering the frequency with a keypad. The type of waveform is set using the *WAVEFORM* switch (or button, or keypad).

A provision may be available to offset the waveform so that it is not centered on zero volts. An *OFFSET* control varies the amount of offset. The offset is adjusted by observing the waveform on the oscilloscope. The oscilloscope must be set for *DC* input so that both the DC and AC components of the waveform are observed. The *AMPLITUDE* or *LEVEL* control varies the output level. Some function generators may be set up entirely with a keypad, or remotely by a computer.

Objectives

This exercise introduces the basic operation of the oscilloscope and function generator. The effect of the instruments control settings will be demonstrated.

Procedure

Equipment and Parts
Oscilloscope, Function Generator, and 100 Ω, 5% resistor

Part 1: Basics

1.   Connect the instruments as shown on the right. Note that the connections are made with "coaxial cables" with "clips" at their ends. The oscilloscope clip may be part of a "probe". Connect the clips as shown below. The clip connected to the ground lead is usually color coded black.

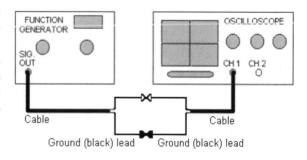

2.   Turn on the oscilloscope, set the *TRIGGER MODE* to "Auto", and establish a single trace (a horizontal line). Set input for channel 1 only, and set the *INPUT COUPLING* to *GND* (the input coupling switch may be under or near the *VOLTS/DIV* switch).

You should see a straight horizontal line (the trace). Adjust the *VERTICAL POSITION* control to center the trace on the screen.

3.   Set the channel 1 *INPUT COUPLING* switch to *DC,* and the *VOLTS/DIV* switch to 1 VOLT/DIV.   Set the *TIME/DIVISION* switch to 10 µS/DIV.

4.   Set the function generator to produce a 4 V peak-to-peak square wave without a DC offset. Set the frequency to exactly 10 KHz.

5.   Set the oscilloscope's trigge*r SLOPE* control to "negative". Adjust the trigger *LEVEL* control for a stable trace, like the one shown below. Notice that the trigger event occurs at the center of the screen. The display may be moved horizontally with the *HORIZONTAL POSITION* control.

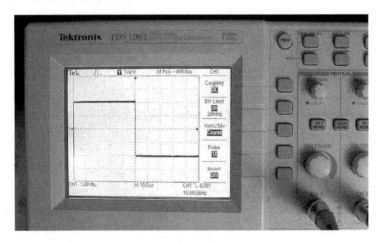

Note the easy to use menu system. The channel 1 menu appeared on the right side of the screen when the *CH1 MENU* button was pressed. The buttons to the right of the screen allow easy selection of channel 1 settings. The channel 2 menu, trigger menu, and horizontal menus work the same way.

6.   The period of a 10 KHz waveform is 100 microseconds (T = 1/f).   The oscilloscope's time base is set to 10 µS/DIV. Since there are 10 horizontal divisions, the total time displayed is 100 µS.   Therefore there is one cycle displayed on the screen (100 microseconds per cycle).

The amplitude display of the function generator may not agree with the amplitude displayed on the oscilloscope. Always use the displayed oscilloscope amplitude as the correct amplitude.

7.   Change the time per division on the oscilloscope to 50 µS/DIV. How many cycles are displayed?

Number of cycles _____4_____

Part 2: Generator Source Resistance

1. The function generator can be modeled as a Thevenin source, as shown below.

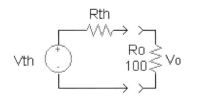

Rth = internal resistance of function generator

Vth = function generator output with no load

Vo = function generator output with a load

2. In part 1, you set the function generator to produce 4 V peak-to-peak without a "load" resistor connected. Therefore Vth is 4 V peak-to-peak since there is no current through Rth and therefore no voltage drop across it. Connect the 100 Ω resistor, Ro, to the function generator without changing any of the settings.

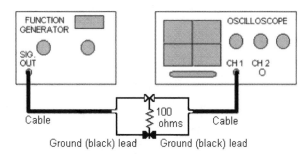

Measure and record the peak-to-peak voltage, Vo, across the 100 Ω resistor. If the generator's internal resistance is about 50 Ω (most are), the voltage should decrease to about two thirds of its former value (2.67 V).

Vo ___2.64___

3. Remove the 100 Ω resistor. Calculate the generator's internal resistance, Rth:

$$Vo = \frac{Ro}{Ro + Rth} Vth.$$ Solving for Rth: $$Rth = Ro\left(\frac{Vth}{Vo} - 1\right)$$ $100\left(\frac{4V}{2.64} - 1\right)$

Rth ___51.5___

Part 3: Settings Exercise

1. Change the function generator waveform to a sine wave. Adjust trigger slope and trigger level controls to get the display shown on the right.
    (f = 10 KHz, v = 4 V peak-to-peak)

    The display on the right was obtained with the trigger slope negative, and trigger level set to zero.

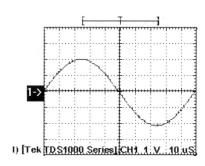

57

2. Note and explain what happens when:

a) Trigger slope is changed to positive (rising). Where is the trigger event on the screen? Why does the waveform's appearance change?

It is opposite (inversed of negative slope)

The trigger phases by π in either negative or positive.

b) Trigger level is changed to +1 V. Where is the trigger event on the screen? Why does the waveform's appearance change?

2/3rds up on the way. The apperance changes

because of the shift

c) Time per division is changed to 100 µS/Div and trigger level to 0 V. Why does the waveform's appearance change?

we are recording more cycles so more are shown

d) Volts per division is changed to 2 V per division. Why does the waveform's appearance change?

1V per division is more zuned in

compared to 2V.

3.   Reset the oscilloscope and function generator to the settings from part 3, step 1. Be sure that the oscilloscope input is set to "DC" coupling.

4a.   Add a +1.00 V offset to the function generator's waveform.   Most function generators will have a button or knob labeled "offset voltage" (you may need to read the instrument's instruction manual).

4b.   Adding a +1 V offset to the waveform should cause it to move vertically on the oscilloscope by 1 V. Note what happens when the oscilloscope's input coupling is set to "AC". Explain your observations below:

---

a.   +1.00 volt offset is added.   Why does the waveform's vertical position change?

       Offsetting makes it to 1 and 5 rather than 0 and 4v.

b.   Input coupling is changed to AC.   Why does the waveform's vertical position change?

       It cause the cycles to be phased.

Lab Check

Your lab instructor will indicate what is required to get credit for this lab exercise. Possibilities include:

1.   Each lab section may be checked and initialed as the exercise is performed.

2.   Entire lab may be checked when the exercise is completed.

3.   A report may be required describing the outcomes of each section.

The lab instructor should be consulted if there is any uncertainty about any of the measurements or instrument settings while doing this lab exercise.

Experiment 15: RC Transient Response

Forced Step Response

Consider the circuit on the right. Before t = 0, the capacitor is discharged and its voltage, v_C, is zero. When the switch is closed at t = 0, the capacitor charges through the resistor and its voltage increases exponentially with time.

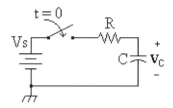

The response of this circuit can be divided into two parts, the "transient response" and the "steady state response".

The transient part occurs while the capacitor is charging and its voltage is changing. The steady state part occurs when the capacitor is fully charged and its voltage stops changing.

This transient response is called a "forced step response", or just "step response", because the voltage applied to the circuit changes value instantly. The capacitor voltage, v_C, as a function of time, is given below.

$$v_C = Vs\,(1 - e^{-\frac{t}{RC}}) + v_C(0)$$

The voltage $v_C(0)$ is the capacitor voltage at t=0. An important parameter of the RC circuit is the "time constant": $\tau = RC$.

Natural Response

Natural response refers to the response of the RC circuit when the circuit is discharging its stored energy. The amount of energy stored in the capacitor can be calculated using the equation below. In the SI system, energy, W, has units of joules, voltage, V, has units of volts, and C has units of farads

$$\text{Capacitor energy: } W = \frac{1}{2}CV^2$$

The capacitor voltage, v_C, as a function of time, is given below.

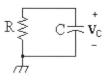

$$v_C = Ve^{-\frac{t}{RC}}. \qquad \text{Capacitor voltage, } v_C = V \text{ at t } = 0.$$

Objectives

The step and natural response of an RC circuit will be measured and compared to calculations. A "square wave" waveform will be used. The generator voltage will alternate between 0 V for 50 µS and 8 V for 50 µS. The voltage stays constant long enough for the circuit to reach "steady state".

When the voltage changes from 0 to 8 V, the circuit's step response will be observed. When it changes from 8 V to 0 V volts, the circuit's natural response will be observed.

Procedure

Equipment and Parts

Oscilloscope, Function Generator, and Breadboard
Resistor: 680 Ω, ¼ watt, 5%. Capacitor: 10 nF, 5%.

---

1. Connect the instruments as shown.

2. Set the function generator to produce a square wave. Set the *FREQUENCY* to 10 KHz.

    Adjust the *AMPLITUDE* and *OFFSET* controls to obtain a 0 to 8 V square wave.

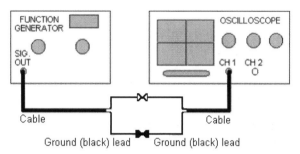

3. Turn on the oscilloscope. Set the *TRIGGER MODE* to "*Auto*". Set the input for channel 1 only, and set the *INPUT COUPLING* to *GND*. The input coupling switch is usually right under, or near, the *VOLTS/DIV* switch, or use the *CH1 MENU* button.

4. Adjust the *VERTICAL POSITION* control so that the trace starts at the bottom of the screen. Set the *INPUT COUPLING* switch to *DC,* and the *VOLTS/DIV switch* to 1 VOLT/DIV. Set the *TIME/DIV* switch to 10µS/DIV.

5. Set the oscilloscope *TRIGGER SLOPE* to negative (falling edge) and *TRIGGER LEVEL* controls to obtain a stable trace. The waveform should begin at the top of the screen (+8 V) and after 50 µS (5 horizontal divisions) it should go to the bottom of the screen (0 V).

6. Connect the RC circuit to the function generator as shown below. Be sure to leave channel 1 of the oscilloscope connected to the function generator.

    The function generator is shown below as a Thevenin equivalent circuit. Vth is the "no load" generator voltage and Rth is the generator's internal resistance. Connect channel 2 of the oscilloscope so that it is across the capacitor to measure Vc, as shown below (display shown is for 5 V peak-to-peak, yours will be 8 V peak-to-peak).

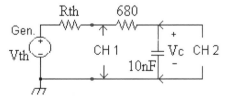

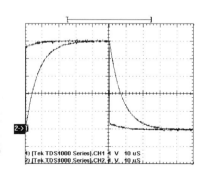

7. Set the oscilloscope to display channel 1 and channel 2 as shown on the right. The left 5 horizontal divisions display the "forced" response of the circuit the right 5 horizontal divisions display the "natural" response.

Notice that the channel 1 waveform has a small dip in it due to the function generator's internal resistance. When the function generator's output goes to 0 V, its internal resistance is still in the circuit. It must be accounted for when calculating the circuit's time constant: $\tau = RC = (Rth + 680)(10nF)$.

8. Change the oscilloscope's *TIME/DIV* to 5μS/DIV. You should see only the forced response. You may need to adjust the *HORIZONTAL POSITION* control to get the display shown below on the right.

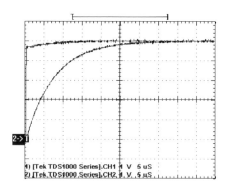

Record the time of occurrence of the predicted voltage for 1, 2, 3, and 4 time constants after t = 0. Use the spreadsheet format given at the bottom of this page. Also see below.

$$1\tau = 8\left(1 - e^{-1}\right) = 8(1-.368) = 5.06 \ volts$$

$$2\tau = 8\left(1 - e^{-2}\right) = 8(1-.135) = 6.92 \ volts$$

$$3\tau = 8\left(1 - e^{-3}\right) = 8(1-.098) = 7.22 \ volts$$

$$4\tau = 8\left(1 - e^{-4}\right) = 8(1-.018) = 7.86 \ volts$$

The horizontal position control has to be adjusted so that the trigger occurs on the left side of the screen to get the display shown above on the right (display shown is for 5 volts peak-to-peak, yours will be 8 volts peak- to-peak).

9. Repeat step 8 above for the circuit's natural response. Keep the oscilloscope's *TIME/DIV* at 5 μSec/DIV, but change the trigger to observe the natural response.

	A	B	C	D	E	F	G	H	I	J	K
1	RC STEP:		Meas.	Calc.			RC NATURAL:		Meas.	Calc.	
2	Tau	Volts	Time	Time	% Error		Tau	Volts	Time	Time	% Error
4	1	5.06					1	2.94			
5	2	6.92					2	1.08			
6	3	7.22					3	0.78			
7	4	7.86					4	0.14			

Analysis

1. Calculate the theoretical time constant values and enter the values into the spreadsheet columns D an J. Calculate the percent error values in columns E and K. You can enter the appropriate equations into the cells in row 4 and use "fill down".

2. Calculate the maximum magnitude and polarity of the circuit current for the circuit's step and natural responses and explain the result.

3.   Simulate the circuit and plot the capacitor voltage and current as a function of time. Refer to the simulation example on the next page.

4.   Compare the measured step and natural response time constants to the simulation results.   How do these compare to the calculation: $\tau = (Rth + R)\, C$?

Lab Report: Include spreadsheet, simulation results, and answers to above questions.

OrCAD PSpice Example: RC Transient Response

The transient response is simulated by using the pulsed voltage source, *"VPULSE"*.   This source generates a square wave. The output is generated using *"Transient"* analysis.

V1's part name is *"VPULSE"* (in the source library).   Double click on the part, inside the circle, to obtain the setup dialog box.   The setup below generates a square wave whose period is 100 µS.

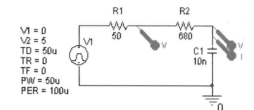

V1 Setup:

DC = 0,   AC = 0,   V1 = 0,   V2 = 5   TD = 0u,   TR = 1n,   TF = 1n,   PW = 50u,   PER = 100u

Analysis type is "Transient" with Print Step = 0.1u, and Final Time = 100u.

Note: Your simulation should have V2 = 8 and should use your measured part values.

The *Probe* output is shown on the right.   The dip in the square wave is due to the 50 Ω source resistance. Details of the response can be obtained using cursors.

For example, the time constant could be determined by using the cursors to measure the times between which the waveform changes from 0.0 V to 63.3% of 5 V (forced response), or the time it takes for the waveform to go from 5 V to 36.7% of 5 V (natural response).

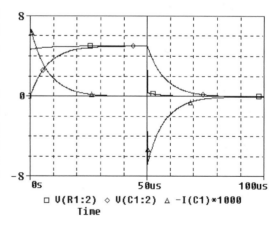

Notice the change in direction of the current. The current is multiplied by 1000 so that it appears on the same graph as the voltage (current scale is in milliamps).

LTspice Example: RC Transient Response

V1 is set by clicking the right mouse button on it and clicking "advanced" in the dialog box shown below.

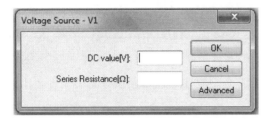

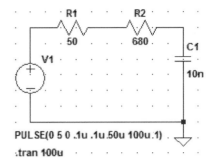

PULSE(0 5 0 .1u .1u .50u 100u .1)

:tran 100u

This will open the dialog box shown on the right. Select *PULSE*.

Enter the desired pulse characteristics. *LTspice* pulse source also has an "*Ncycles*" parameter.

Select transient analysis with a stop time of 100 μS and maximum time step of 0.1 μS.

Placing the mouse pointer over a part after running the simulation displays an arrow which shows the direction of positive current.

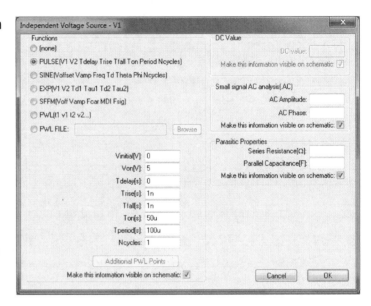

The graph below on the left shows the capacitor voltage and the voltage between R1 and R2. Click the probe on the nodes where you wish to see the voltage. The graph below on the right shows the capacitor current. Move the mouse over the capacitor and click to display the current waveform.

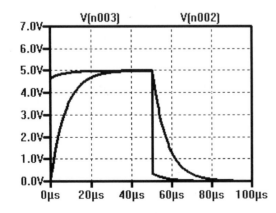

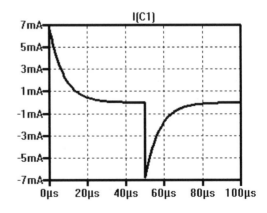

Experiment 16: Capacitor Network Transient Response

Introduction

Series connected capacitors receive the same current when charged. Each capacitor will have the same charge Q, regardless of the value of its capacitance. However the voltage across each capacitor will depend on its capacitance.

Consider the circuit on the right.   The voltage across the two capacitors, V1 + V2, will be close to 10 volts if the switch is closed for more than 5 time constants.

Given that C1 = 10 nF and C2 = 40 nF, find V1 and V2:

$$C_T = \frac{10 \cdot 40}{10 + 40}\,nF = 8\,nF \qquad\qquad Q_T = Q_1 = Q_2 = C_T \cdot Vs = (8\,nF) \cdot (10\,Volts) = 80\,nC$$

$$V_1 = \frac{Q_1}{C_1} = \frac{80nC}{10nF} = 8\,V \qquad\qquad V_2 = \frac{Q_2}{C_2} = \frac{80nC}{40nF} = 2\,V$$

The RC time constant of the circuit is determined by C_T and R and is equal to 80 microseconds in this case.

Objectives

This experiment demonstrates the transient response of an RC circuit with two series connected capacitors. It will show that all of the capacitors in the capacitor network charge at the same rate, which is determined by the net capacitance of the network, C_T, and the circuit resistance, R.

Procedure

Equipment and Parts
Function Generator, Oscilloscope, and Breadboard. 10 nF, 22 nF, 5% capacitors, 10k resistor, ¼ watt, 5%.

1.   Connect the circuit on the right

2.   Set the generator to produce a 5 Khz, 10 V peak-to-peak square wave with a plus 5-volt offset.

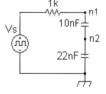

3.   Connect oscilloscope channel 1 to node n1. Set the trigger to channel 1.

   Connect oscilloscope channel 2 to node n2. Set the oscilloscope time base to display one cycle of the response. Both channels should be set to DC input coupling.

4.   Adjust the oscilloscope display so that you can accurately measure the response time constants, T_1 and T_2, and steady state peak-to-peak amplitudes of V_1 and V_2 at nodes n1 and n2.   The steady state amplitude occurs after 5 time constants when the capacitor is fully charged. Record below:

T_1 _____ V_1 _____

T_2 _____ V_2 _____

Analysis

1.   Use the results of step 4 to calculate the steady state charge on the 10 nF capacitor (5 time constants after Vs = 0).

2.   Calculate the theoretical value of the steady state charge on the 10 nF capacitor and compare the results to step 1 above.

3.   Use the results of step 4 to calculate the steady charge on the 2 2nF capacitor.

4.   Calculate the theoretical value of the steady state charge on the 22 nF capacitor and compare the results to step 3 above.

5.   Explain why the oscilloscope waveform on channel 2 goes negative.

6.   Calculate the circuit's time constant, and compare the result to your measurement. How do the time constants for the 10 nF and 22 nF capacitors compare and why?

7.   Simulate the circuit and compare the simulated results to your measurements. Explain any differences.

Simulation Example: PSpice

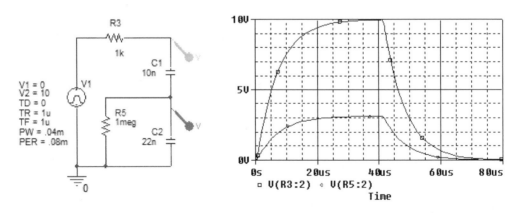

A one megohm resistor is placed across C2 to avoid a "floating node" error. The one megohm resistor also simulates the input resistance of an oscilloscope when using a 1X probe.

Experiment 17: Superposition of AC and DC Voltages

Introduction

Superposition of AC and DC voltages is very common in electronic circuits. The AC component may be a signal carrying information, an AC power line voltage, or it may be an undesired "noise" voltage. The DC component may be a voltage necessary for the operation of a transistor amplifier, or the output of a DC power supply.

A coupling capacitor will pass an AC voltage, but block a DC voltage. The capacitor does provide opposition to current flow similar to a resistor. The capacitor's "resistance" is frequency dependent and is called "capacitive reactance." Its value, X_C, is given by:

$$X_C = \frac{1}{2\pi f C}$$

C is capacitance in farads and f is frequency in hertz.

Objectives

The effect of voltage dividers and capacitors on AC and DC voltages will be investigated.

Procedure

+---
| **Equipment and Parts**
|
| Oscilloscope, Function Generator, and Breadboard.
| Resistors: R1=1K, R2=1K, and R3=1.2K, all ¼ watt, 5%.
| Capacitor: 100 nF, 5%.
+---

Part 1: DC Measurements

1. Measure the resistors: R1 _____ R2 _____ R3 _____

2. Connect the circuit on the right. Connect oscilloscope channel 1 to node N1 and channel 2 to node N2.

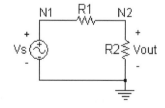

3. Set the coupling on both channels to "GND". Set the trigger to channel 1 and to "auto". Set both traces to the center of the screen with the vertical position controls.

    Set channel 1 and channel 2 to 1 V/DIV.
    Change the coupling on both channels to DC.
    Set the time base to 2.5 µS/DIV (or 2 µS/DIV).

    Set the generator to produce a 3.0 V peak-to-peak, 100 KHz sine wave with a +1.5 V offset.

    Important: Use the oscilloscope to set the amplitude and offset of the sine wave. Your oscilloscope display should be similar to the one shown on the right.

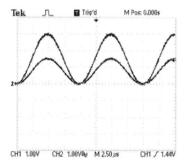

The function generator with a DC offset can be represented by a DC voltage source in series with an AC voltage source as shown on the right.

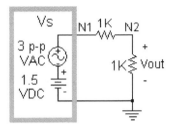

4. Measure the DC voltages at nodes N1 and N2 with a DMM. Record below:

    VDC$_{N1}$ _____ VDC$_{N2}$ _____

5. Change the coupling on both oscilloscope channels to AC. This removes the DC component from the oscilloscope. Both waveforms should be centered on 0.0 volts.

6. Change both vertical channels to 0.5 V/DIV. Measure the peak-to-peak AC voltages at nodes N1 and N2 with the oscilloscope. Record below:

    VAC$_{N1}$ _____ VAC$_{N2}$ _____

Part 2: AC Superposition

1. Connect the circuit on the right. Connect channel 1 to node N1 and channel 2 to node N3.

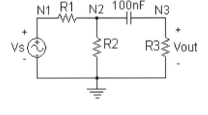

2. Set the coupling on both channels to "GND". Set the trigger to channel 1 and to "auto". Center both traces.

    Set channel 1 and channel 2 to 1 V/DIV.
    Set the coupling on both channels to DC.
    Set the timing to 2.5 µS/DIV (or 2 µS/DIV).

    Set the generator to produce a 3.0 V peak-to-peak, 100 KHz sine wave with a +1.5 V offset.

    Important: Use the oscilloscope to set the amplitude and offset of the sine wave.   Your display should be similar to the one on the right.

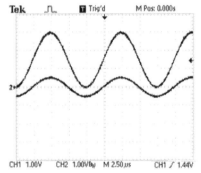

3. Set vertical channel 2 to 200 mV/DIV. Measure and record the peak-to-peak voltage at node N3.

    VAC$_{N3}$ _____

4. Set channel 2 to 500 mV/DIV and the coupling to DC. Connect channel 2 to node N2. Determine the average voltage, V_{AVE}, of the sine wave by algebraically adding the value of its positive and negative peak and dividing by 2.

    V$_{AVE}$ _____

5. Set vertical channel 2 to 200 mV/DIV and change the coupling to AC. Measure and record the peak-to-peak amplitude of the voltage at node N2.

    VAC$_{N2}$ _____

6.   Measure the DC voltages at nodes N1, N2, and N3 with a DMM. Record below:

VDC$_{N1}$ _____ VDC$_{N2}$ _____ VDC$_{N3}$ _____

Analysis

1.   Show that the results of part 1 can be theoretically calculated using the superposition principle. Model the source as a 1.5 V DC source in series with a 3 V peak-to-peak AC source. Calculate the percent difference between the measured and calculated values of: VDC$_{N2}$ and VAC$_{N2}$.

2.   Show that the results of procedure part 2 can be theoretically calculated using the superposition principle. Model the source as a 1.5 V DC source in series with a 3 V peak-to-peak AC source. Hint: Consider the capacitor an open circuit for DC and a short (closed) circuit for AC. Calculate the percent difference between the measured and calculated values of: VAC$_{N2}$, VAC$_{N3}$, VDC$_{N2}$, VDC$_{N3}$ and V$_{AVE}$.

Given that: $X_C = \dfrac{1}{2\pi f C}$, $X_C = \infty$ at f = 0 (DC), and $X_C = 16\Omega$ at f = 100KHz.

3.   Simulate the circuit of part 2 and compare the results to your measurements and calculations.

Example PSpice Simulation Results for Part 2

V1 is named "VSIN" in the "Source" library.
Analysis type is "Time Domain" (Transient).
Run to time is 20 µsec.

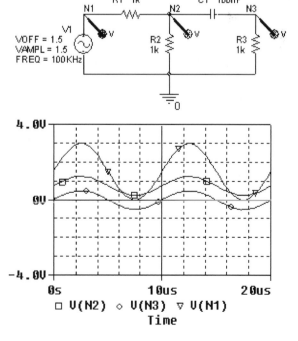

Note the results in the plot on the right.
The AC amplitude at nodes N2 and N3 is the same. However, the DC component is removed by the capacitor between nodes N2 and N3.

69

Example LTspice simulation results for part 2

V1 was set by right clicking on it, setting "Functions" to SINE, DC offset to 1.5, Amplitude to 1.5, Frequency to 100k, and Cycles to 2.

Simulation was set to "Transient", with Stop Time of 20u and Maximum Timestep of .1u.

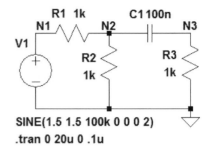

SINE(1.5 1.5 100k 0 0 0 2)
.tran 0 20u 0 .1u

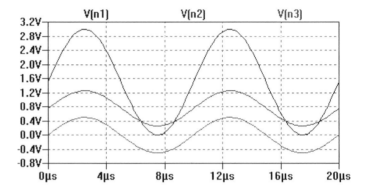

After running the simulation, the graph on the right was obtained by moving the mouse to each node and clicking when the probe appears.

You can also click on "Plot Settings" in the main menu and select "Visible Traces". The window shown on the right will open. Select the three nodes by holding down the "Shift Key" while making the selections.

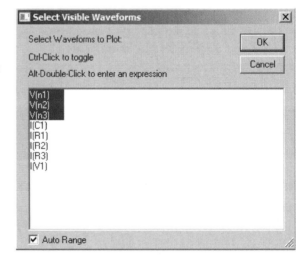

AC Lab Notes: Working with Phasors

A sinusoidal voltage has a value that is a function of time and may be generally expressed as:

$$v = V\sin(\omega t + \theta) \qquad \text{or} \qquad v = V\cos(\omega t + \theta).$$

The angle "θ" is usually expressed in degrees. However, the angle "ωt" has units of radians. To evaluate the argument of the sine or cosine, convert angle "ωt" to degrees, then add "θ".

Figure 1 below shows phasor V_a rotating counter clockwise at angular velocity ω. The value of V_a at time t is its vertical component at time t, and is equal to v_a. Figure 1 shows that v_a equals 0 when t is zero. It reaches a maximum when t equals 0.25 mSec.

Figure 2 below also shows phasor V_a rotating counter clockwise at an angular velocity ω. The value of V_a at time t is its vertical component at time t, which is a cosine function of t and is equal to v_a. Figure 2 shows v_a maximum when t is zero, and zero when t equals 0.25 mSec.

Observations:

Period T of V_a=1.0 mS.
Frequency f =1 KHz.
Frequency ω=6283 r/S.

Phasors in polar form for both figure 1 and figure 2:

$$V_a = |V_a| \angle 0^\circ$$

$$V_b = |V_b| \angle \theta^\circ$$

The only difference between Figure 1 and Figure 2 is the reference time t = 0. The phasors in Figure 1 and Figure 2 are identical.

Some textbooks choose the sine function as reference and others use the cosine function to describe sinusoids. As is shown here, the phasor description is identical.

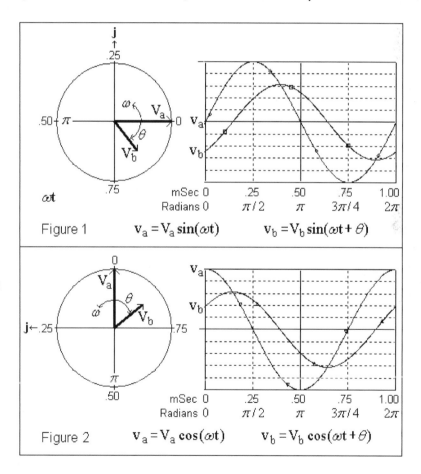

Figure 1 $v_a = V_a \sin(\omega t)$ $v_b = V_b \sin(\omega t + \theta)$

Figure 2 $v_a = V_a \cos(\omega t)$ $v_b = V_b \cos(\omega t + \theta)$

Some textbooks express the magnitude of a phasor in RMS units rather than peak units. Observe the textbook's conventions when working textbook problems.

It is important to be able to recognize the convention used in contexts outside of your textbook. It is essential to include the units when expressing results, for example:

$V_a = 5\angle 30^0$ volts peak, $V_a = 3.53\angle 30^0$ volts rms, $I_a = 4.6\angle 40^0$ mA peak-to-peak.

Magnitudes and Angles in PSpice

In PSpice, the magnitude of a sinusoidal source is expressed in peak units. See the example below where the source amplitude is set to 5 V. Transient analysis displays the magnitudes of the sinusoids as 5 V peak, or 10 V peak-to-peak. You can set the phase angle of the source by double clicking on it. This opens the property editor to specify the phase angle at t = 0. The phase angle of V2 was set to 90 degrees, resulting in a cosine waveform.

The first cycle of the waveforms at nodes n1 and n2 differ from the second cycle. It usually takes a few cycles for the waveforms to reach steady state (where each cycle is the same.)

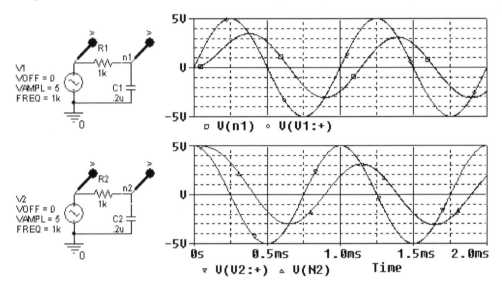

A non-transient source, such as "VAC" is used when using printers in PSpice. The analysis frequencies are set in the "Sweep Analysis" dialog box. Double clicking on the source allows you to set the phase angle at t = 0. Double clicking on the printers allows you to set the type of measurement to be made. Usually the word "ok" is typed under "AC", "Magnitude", and "Phase Angle". The phase angle is expressed in degrees. However, the units for magnitude will be the same as the units used for the source.

For example, if you set the amplitude of the source to 5 V peak, then the magnitudes of the results will be in units of volts-peak. You decide what the units for the source are. If you decide to use rms units for the magnitude of the source, then all the results expressed by the printers will be in rms units. Peak-to-peak units are often used in the laboratory since that is the most accurate measurement unit on the oscilloscope.

Experiment 18: AC Measurements / Series RC Circuit

Introduction

Capacitance has two important properties in circuit analysis. One property is that the voltage developed across a capacitor by a steady state sinusoidal current will be lagging the current by 90 degrees. The other property is called "capacitive reactance", X_C. It is inversely proportional to the frequency of the applied sinusoid.

$$X_C = \frac{1}{2\pi f C}$$ ohms. f is the frequency in hertz. C is the capacitance in farads.

A series RC circuit provides an opposition to current flow called "impedance". Since the elements are in series the impedance, Z, is given by: **Z = R - jX$_C$**.

The current, **I**, can be calculated with Ohm's Law: **I = V$_S$/Z**.

In a series circuit, **I** is the same in each element. **V$_S$ = V$_R$ + V$_C$**, and **IZ = IR + I(-jX$_C$)**.

Objectives

A steady state sinusoidal voltage will be applied to a series connected RC circuit. The amplitude and phase angle of voltages in the RC circuit will be measured. The measurements will be compared to theoretical calculations.

Procedure

Equipment and Parts

Function Generator, Oscilloscope, and Breadboard.
C = 100 nF, 5% capacitor, R = 1000 Ω, ¼ watt, 5%.

The voltage V_R is in phase with the circuit current in Figures A and B below. The circuit in Figure B is used to measure V_C. The resistor and capacitor swap positions to keep the oscilloscope and function generator grounds together. Figure C shows the phase relationship of the circuit voltages with respect to the source, V_S.

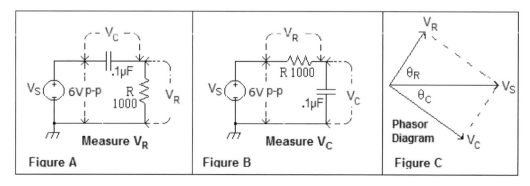

Figure A — Measure V_R Figure B — Measure V_C Figure C — Phasor Diagram

1. Measure and record the value of R and C (if possible).

    R_____   C_____

    Connect the circuit in Figure A.   Connect oscilloscope channel 1 to measure V_S and channel 2 to measure V_R. Set channel 1 and channel 2 to 1 V/DIV. Set the time base to 100 µS/DIV. Trigger on channel 1. Set the generator to produce a 1000 Hz, 6 V peak-to-peak sine wave with no offset.

2. Adjust the oscilloscope for a display similar to Figure D below. V_S starts at 0 V with a positive slope at the left side of the screen. The "MEASURE" feature is used to measure the peak-to-peak voltages. The cursors are used to measure the time each trace crosses 0 V with a negative slope. Record below:

    V_R _____volts peak-to-peak

3. Note that the period of the sinusoid is exactly 1000 µS. V_R crosses zero 160 µS before V_S. Therefore V_R leads V_S. The angle can be calculated by the proportion:

$$\frac{160\mu S}{1000\mu S} = \frac{\theta_R}{360^0} \quad \text{or}: \ \theta_R = \left(\frac{160\mu S}{1000\mu S}\right)360^0 = 57.6^0.$$

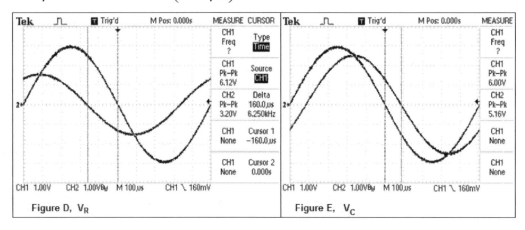

Figure D, V_R

Figure E, V_C

    Measure and record the value of θ_R and record below:

    θ_R _____degrees

4. Connect the circuit in Figure B on page 73 (swap the positions of the resistor and capacitor).   Connect oscilloscope channel 1 to measure V_S and channel 2 to measure V_C. Set channel 1 and channel 2 to 1 V/DIV. Set the time base to 100 µS/DIV and Trigger on channel 1. Set the function generator to produce a 1000 Hz, 6 V, peak-to-peak sine wave with no offset.

5. Adjust the oscilloscope for a display similar to Figure E above. Record below:

    V_C _____volts peak-to-peak

6. Determine the phase angle, θ_C, and record below:

θ_C _____ degrees

In Figure E, V_C crosses zero 89 μS after V_S. Therefore V_C lags V_S.

$$\theta_C = \left(\frac{-89\,\mu S}{1000\,\mu S}\right)360^0 = -32.1^0.$$

Analysis

1. Calculate the theoretical value (magnitude and phase angle) of the current, **I**, in the series RC circuit. Calculate the percent difference between the measured and calculated value of **I** (use Ohm's Law and the voltage measured across R to calculate the measured value of **I**).

2. Calculate the theoretical value (magnitude and phase angle) of the voltages, $\mathbf{V_R}$ and $\mathbf{V_C}$, in the series RC circuit. Calculate the percent difference between the measured and calculated value of $\mathbf{V_R}$ and $\mathbf{V_C}$.

3. Simulate the series RC circuit using OrCAD PSpice or LTspice to obtain the magnitude and phase angle of $\mathbf{V_R}$ and $\mathbf{V_C}$. See examples below:

PSpice Example

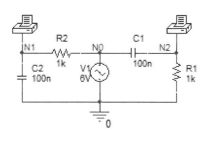 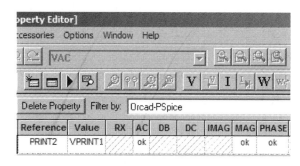

Each printer in the diagram above must be enabled. Double click on each printer and enter an "ok" under AC, MAG, and PHASE (see above).

Select Analysis Type: AC Sweep/Noise. AC Sweep Type: Linear.
Start frequency = 1000 Hz. Stop frequency = 1000 Hz. Total Points = 1.

View the "Output File" to see the results. See edited results below:

FREQ	VM(N2)	VP(N2)
1.000E+03	3.192E+00	5.786E+01

FREQ	VM(N1)	VP(N1)
1.000E+03	5.080E+00	-3.214E+01

LTspice Example

Connect the circuit as shown on the right.

Right click on V1and set "AC amplitude" to 6 under "Small signal AC analysis" in the dialog box that opens.

Labeling the nodes (N1, N2, and N0) makes it easier to interpret the results.

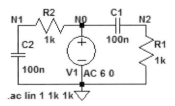

Click on Simulate in the main menu bar.

Select *Edit Simulation Cmd*, to open the dialog box shown on the right.

Select *AC Analysis* and enter values as shown. Note that this is for one frequency. You can specify the simulation to be done at more than one frequency, if desired.

Run the simulation. A window will open listing the simulation results.

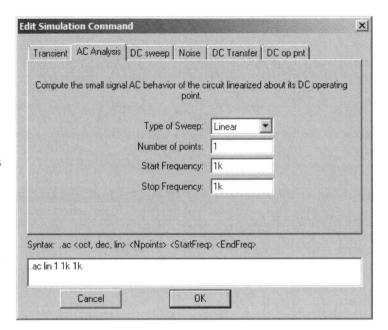

```
         --- AC Analysis ---


    frequency:      1000          Hz
    V(n2):          mag:   3.19211 phase:    57.8581°          voltage
    V(n0):          mag:         6 phase: -4.24074e-015°       voltage
    V(n1):          mag:    5.0804 phase:   -32.1419°          voltage
```

Experiment 19: AC Measurements / Series RL Circuit

Introduction

Inductance has two important properties in circuit analysis. One property is that the voltage developed across an inductor by a steady state sinusoidal current will be leading the current by 90 degrees. The other is called "inductive reactance, X_L. It is directly proportional to the frequency of the applied sinusoid and has units of ohms.

$X_L = \omega L = 2\pi f L$ ohms, where f is the frequency in hertz and L is the inductance in henries.

At low frequencies an inductor may be approximated by an inductance in series with a resistance, R_W. This resistance is mainly due to the wire winding of the inductor. This resistance does increase with frequency, but it is approximately constant for frequencies used in the experiments in this manual (below 10 KHz.).

Refer to the series RL circuit at the bottom of this page. The impedance, Z, of the circuit is given by: $Z = (R + R_W) + jX_L$. The current, I, can be calculated with Ohm's law: $I = V_S/Z$.
In a series circuit, I is the same in each element. The voltage across the inductance in the diagrams below can't be measured directly, but V_X can be measured. $V_X = I(R_W + jX_L)$.

Objectives

A steady state sinusoidal voltage will be applied to a series connected RL circuit. The amplitude and phase angle of voltages in the RL circuit will be measured. The measurements will be compared to theoretical calculations.

Procedure

+---+
| **Equipment and Parts** |
| |
| Function Generator, Oscilloscope, and Breadboard. |
| Inductor: 100 mH, 5%, Resistor: 1000 Ω, ¼ watt, 5%. |
+---+

Consider Figure A below. The voltage V_R is in phase with the circuit current. The circuit in Figure B below is used to measure V_X. The resistor and inductor swap positions to keep the oscilloscope and function generator grounds together.

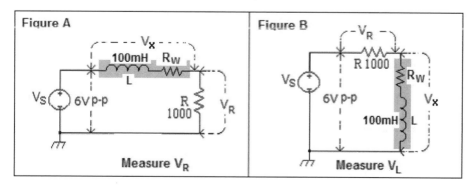

1. Measure and record the value of R, R_W, and L (if possible).

   R _____ R_W _____   L _____

2. Connect the circuit in Figure A. Connect oscilloscope channel 1 to measure V_S and channel 2 to measure V_R. Set channel 1 and channel 2 to 1 V/DIV. Set the time base to 100 μS/DIV and Trigger to channel 1. Set the function generator to produce a 1000 Hz, 6 V peak-to-peak sine wave with no offset as measured by the oscilloscope channel 1.

3. Measure and record the peak-to-peak voltage, V_R _____.

4. Measure and record the value of θ_R _____.

5. Connect the circuit in Figure B on page 77 (swap the positions of the resistor and inductor). Connect oscilloscope channel 1 to measure V_S and channel 2 to measure V_X. Set channel 1 and channel 2 to 1 V/DIV. Set the time base to 100 μS/DIV and Trigger on channel 1. Set the function generator to produce a 1000 Hz, 6 V peak-to-peak sine wave with no offset as measured by the oscilloscope channel 1.

6. Measure and record the peak-to-peak voltage, V_X _____.

7. Measure and record the value of θ_X _____

8. Optional: Repeat this exercise at another frequency, such as 500 Hz or 2000 Hz.

Analysis

1. Calculate the theoretical value (magnitude and phase angle) of the current, I, in the series RL circuit. Calculate the percent difference between the measured and calculated value of I (use the voltage measured across R). Note that you need to include R_W in the calculations.

2. Calculate the theoretical value (magnitude and phase angle) of the voltages, V_R and V_X, in the series RL circuit. Calculate the percent difference between the measured and calculated value of V_R and V_X.

3. Simulate the circuit using PSpice or LTspice to obtain the magnitude and phase angle of the voltages: V_R and V_X. Compare your results to your calculations. They should be in almost exact agreement. Express the percent difference between your measurements and calculations.

Experiment 20: Series-Parallel AC Circuit Measurements

Introduction

Refer to the circuit on the right. The impedance of this circuit is given by:

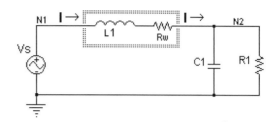

$$Z = (Rw + j\omega L1) + Z_P, \text{ where: } Z_P = \frac{-jR1\left(\frac{1}{\omega C1}\right)}{R1 - j\left(\frac{1}{\omega C1}\right)}.$$

Rw is the resistance of the inductor. The voltage at node N2 can be calculated using Ohm's Law. First calculate the circuit current, I: $I = Vs/Z$.

Then calculate the voltage developed by that current across the impedance of the parallel combination of C1 and R1. $V_{N2} = I \cdot Z_P$.

Objectives

A steady state sinusoidal voltage will be applied to a series-parallel connected RLC circuit. The amplitudes and phase angles of voltages and currents in the circuit will be measured. The measurements will be compared to theoretical calculations.

Procedure

Equipment and Parts

Function Generator, Oscilloscope with 10X probes, and Breadboard.
Resistor: 4.7K, ¼ watt, 5%, Inductor: 100 mH, 5%, Capacitor: 0.1 µF, 5%.

---

1. Measure and record the values of the components, including the resistance of the inductor, Rw.

   R1 _____   Rw _____   L _____   C _____

2. Connect the circuit on the right. Connect oscilloscope channel 1 to N1 and channel 2 to N2. Set the trigger to channel 1.

3.. Set the generator to produce a 3.0 V peak-to-peak, 800 Hz, sine wave at node N1.

4. Measure and record the peak-to-peak magnitude and phase angle of the voltage at node N2 (ch2). Record your results into the data table on the next page.

Data Table

Freq. Hz	V_{N1} p-p	VP_{N1} deg.	V_{N2} p-p	VP_{N2} deg.	I_{N2} p-p	IP_{N2} deg.
800.00	3.00	0.00				
1600.00	3.00	0.00				
3200.00	3.00	0.00				

5.   Set the function generator to produce a 3.0 V peak-to-peak, 1600 Hz, sine wave, as measured by channel 1 of the oscilloscope. Repeat step 4.

6.   Set the function generator to produce a 3.0 V peak-to-peak, 3200 Hz, sine wave, as measured by channel 1 of the oscilloscope. Repeat step 4.

Analysis

1.   Use the voltage measurements at node N2 to calculate the circuit current, I, at each frequency. Enter the results into the table above.

2.   Use your scientific calculator to calculate inductive and capacitive reactance at each frequency. Then calculate the impedance of the circuit, **Z**, at each frequency, using the measured values of your components.

TI-89 example at 1600 Hz:

X_{L1}: 2*π*1600*.1 = 1005 ohms. X_{C1}: = 1/(2*π*1600*.1E-6) = 995 ohms.

Z: 100+1005i+(-4700*995i)/(4700-995i) = (306.2∠ 9.91).

3.   Use Ohm's law to calculate the circuit current, I, at each frequency.

I: 3/(306.2∠ 9.91) = (9.80∠-9.91).

4.   Simulate the circuit. Compare the simulated results to your calculations. They should agree exactly. Express the percent difference between your calculated and measured current and between your calculated and measured node 2 voltage.

PSpice Example

Connect the circuit as shown on the right.

The printers, "IPRINT" and "VPRINT1", are in the "SPECIAL" library.

Enable the printers by double clicking on each printer to open the property editor. Type "ok" under AC, MAG, and PHASE.

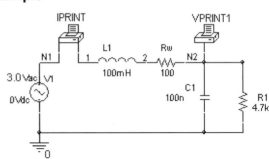

Simulation Settings: Analysis type: AC SWEEP/Noise, Sweep Type: Log/Octave,
Start Frequency: 800, End frequency = 3200, Points/Octave: 1.

Output File Results:

FREQ	IM(V_PRINT2)	IP(V_PRINT2)
8.000E+02	2.088E-03	5.550E+01
1.600E+03	9.800E-03	-1.001E+01
3.200E+03	1.965E-03	-8.428E+01

FREQ	VM(N2)	VP(N2)
8.000E+02	3.824E+00	-1.156E+01
1.600E+03	9.536E+00	-8.806E+01
3.200E+03	9.722E-01	-1.682E+02

LTspice Example

Connect the circuit on the right.   Use your
measured part values.

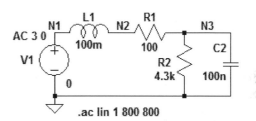

Right click on V1and set "AC amplitude" to 6 under
"Small signal AC analysis" in the dialog box that
opens.

Labeling the nodes (N1, N2, and N0) makes it
easier to interpret the results.

Click on Simulate in the main menu.

Select *Edit Simulation Cmd* to open the
dialog box shown on the right.

Select *AC Analysis* and enter values as
shown. Note that this is for one
frequency. If you specify more than one
frequency the output of the simulation will
be a graph instead of a list.

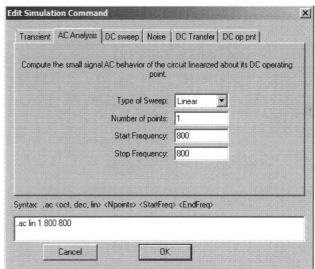

You will need to run the simulation three
times, once for each frequency. Run the
simulation. A window will open listing the
simulation results.

```
        --- AC Analysis ---
frequency:     800          Hz
V(n3):      mag:    3.80461 phase:   -12.2394°        voltage
V(n1):      mag:          3 phase:        0°          voltage
I(V1):      mag: 0.00210717 phase:  -127.067°         device_current
```

The results for the voltages should agree with your expectations. The currents need to be
interpreted according to LTspice conventions.

Experiment 21: RLC Steady State Sinusoidal Response

Introduction

When applied to an electric circuit connected to a sinusoidal source, the term "steady state" means that the sinusoidal source has been applied to the circuit for a long enough time so that the magnitudes and phase angles of the voltages and currents in the circuit have stopped changing with time.

Steady state conditions are usually reached within the first few cycles after the source is applied. When making measurements, the circuit voltages and currents will usually have reached steady state conditions way before the measurements can be made.

Objectives

This exercise will demonstrate how to make AC voltage magnitude and phase angle measurements, and how to perform a simulation of the circuit. Circuit measurements will be made at 3 frequencies: 10 KHz, 20 KHz, and 30 KHz. The circuit's AC steady state response will be simulated at these frequencies. The measured and simulated results will be compared.

Procedure

Equipment and Parts
Oscilloscope, Function Generator, Breadboard. Resistors: 470 Ω, 5%, 1 KΩ, all ¼ watt, 5% Capacitor: 10 nF, 5%. Inductor: 10 mH, 5% (air core preferred).

1. Connect the circuit below (Rx is the resistance of the inductor). Layout the circuit on the breadboard like the diagram, as in the picture below.

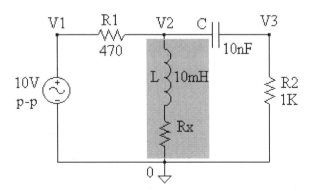 

2. Connect channel 1 of the oscilloscope to measure V1. Set the function generator to produce a 10 volt peak-to-peak sine wave with no offset at exactly 10.00 KHz. Use the oscilloscope to set the amplitude.

The oscilloscope should be set as follows:

VERTICAL: Channel 1   Volts/DIV = 2   Coupling = AC   TRIGGER: Channel 1
Mode = Auto   Coupling = AC   HORIZONTAL: Time/DIV. = 10 µs/div.

3.   Connect channel 2 of the oscilloscope to measure
V3. Adjust the trigger and centering controls to
obtain a display similar the one shown on the right.

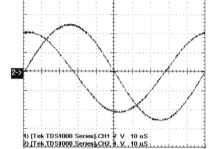

Adjust the trigger controls so that the sinusoid
displayed on channel 1 starts on the left side of the
screen at zero amplitude.

Both wave forms are centered.

Set the vertical coupling to GND on both channels to
center the traces. Observe the phase difference between channels.

4.   One cycle of the sinusoid on channel 1 should begin at 0 volts and have a positive
slope on the left side of the screen, and also 0 volts and a positive slope at the right
side of the screen. Since one cycle is 360^0, and there are 10 divisions across the
screen, each division represents 36^0

The display above shows the channel 2 sinusoid crossing the zero volt axis with a
negative slope 2.2 horizontal divisions before the channel 1 reference sinusoid.
Therefore channel 2 leads channel 1 by about 2.2 times 36^0, or about 79^0.

Another method could be used which can be done with more accuracy.   Measure the
period of the reference sinusoid.   Then measure the time difference   between the
zero axis crossings of both sinusoids, t_z (be sure that they both have the same slope
at the zero crossings).   The phase angle can then be expressed as:

$$\theta = \frac{t_z}{T} 360^0$$

*The TIME/DIVISION controls can be used to measure t_z more accurately. If the
frequency is known accurately, the period T can be calculated:* $T = 1/f$.

5.   Measure and record the magnitudes and phase angles of the voltages, V2 and V3, at
the frequencies of 10 KHz, 20 KHz, and 30 KHz.

Frequency	V2 Magnitude	V2 Angle	V3 Magnitude	V3 Angle
10k	7.60	2.60	4.48	8.5
20k	7.40	6.264	6.1	4.1
30k	7.24	2.1	6.34	3.0

Use the VOLTS/DIVISION control on channel 2 to get the largest vertical displacement of the waveform. This increases the accuracy of both the magnitude and phase measurements. Also, make sure that both waveforms are centered vertically.

6.   You should have 3 sets of voltage and phase measurements for V2 and V3, one set for each frequency. Enter your data into a spreadsheet, formatted as shown below. Fill in the rest of the spreadsheet after you do the simulation.

Frequency	Measured V2 p-p		Simulated V2 p-p		Percent Error, V2	
KiloHertz	Magnitude	Phase	Magnitude	Phase	Magnitude	Phase
10						
20						
30						
Frequency	Measured V3 p-p		Simulated V3 p-p		Percent Error, V3	
KiloHertz	Magnitude	Phase	Magnitude	Phase	Magnitude	Phase
10						
20						
30						

Analysis

1.   Use *PSpice* to simulate your circuit at the frequencies of 10 KHz, 20 KHz, and 30 KHz. Refer to the example simulation on the next page.

2.   Use the spreadsheet to compare the measured data to the *PSpice* simulation.

3.   Discuss the accuracy of your results. It is usually harder to measure the actual values of the inductor and capacitor you used in this experiment. There are instruments that can measure capacitance accurately, but the problem with inductance measurements is that the inductance can vary with frequency and inductor current. To reduce the uncertainty in inductance, use an air core inductor with a 5% or better accuracy.

     Given all the variables, your measured results should be within about 10% of your simulated results.

4.   Optional: Use the "node voltage" method and *Maple* to calculate the values of V2 and V3 at the frequency of 10 KHz. Your calculated results should agree with the results of the simulation.

PSpice Example: RLC Circuit Phasor Analysis

The circuit below is simulated at three frequencies by the "AC SWEEP" feature of *PSpice*. The magnitudes and phase angles of the voltages at the circuit nodes, V2 and V3, are measured by the printers for each frequency.

Printers in the schematic read the voltages with respect to ground, and list their values in the "Output File". Phase angles are with respect to the source, V1.

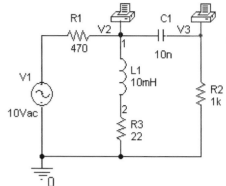

The part name for the printers is: "VPRINT1". Double click on each printer and set the following: AC = ok, MAG = ok, and PHASE = ok.

V1 is a source whose part name is: "Vac". Set V1 to: ACMAG = 10V, ACPHASE = 0, DC = 0.

Set the Simulation Settings: Analysis type = AC SWEEP/ NOISE.
AC Sweep Type = Linear, Total Points = 3, Start Frequency = 10k, End Frequency = 30k.

Run the simulation. When done, click on "View" in the *Probe* menu bar and select "Output File".

Analysis Results:

**** AC ANALYSIS   TEMPERATURE =   27.000 DEG C

FREQ	VM(V2)	VP(V2)
1.000E+04	7.832E+00	2.479E+01
2.000E+04	7.678E+00	6.388E+00
3.000E+04	7.295E+00	2.288E+00

FREQ	VM(V3)	VP(V3)
1.000E+04	4.167E+00	8.265E+01
2.000E+04	6.008E+00	4.490E+01
3.000E+04	6.444E+00	3.023E+01

Using Probe to Plot the Frequency Response

A plot of the voltage and phase response at any node may be obtained by increasing the number of points in the frequency range. "Markers" at the nodes cause Probe to plot the response. The "Voltage Level" marker plots the magnitude of the voltage and the "Phase of Voltage" marker plots the phase angle.

Note the "V" and "VP" markers on node V3 in the diagram on the right.

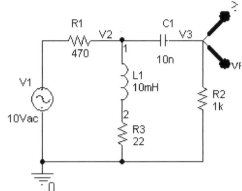

Set the Simulation Settings:
Analysis type = AC SWEEP/ NOISE.
AC Sweep Type = Linear.
Total Points = 100.
Start Frequency = 10k.
End Frequency = 30k.

Analysis Results:

The Probe output is shown on the right.

Voltage magnitude of V3 starts at about 4.2 volts at 10 KHz and increases to about 6.5 volts at 30 KHz.

Phase angle of V3 starts at about 82 degrees at 10 Khz and decreases to about 31 degrees at 30 Khz.

Cursors could be used to read the voltage magnitude and phase angle more accurately.

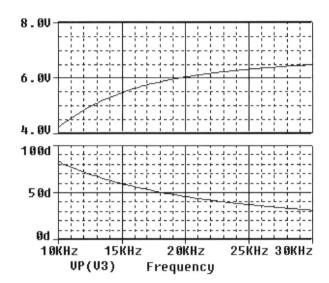

86

Experiment 22: Capacitive Voltage Dividers

Introduction

Voltage dividers may incorporate inductors and capacitors as well as resistors. Since inductive and capacitive reactance are frequency dependent, the voltage division may also be frequency dependent. In addition, there may be a frequency dependent phase shift. Capacitive voltage dividers are widely used in communications circuits.

We will investigate the characteristics of a capacitive voltage divider. The circuit in Figure A below consists of a resistive divider, R1 and R2, and a capacitive divider, C1 and C2. The output voltages of these dividers may be written as:

$$V_{N1} = \frac{R2}{R1+R2}6V\,p-p,$$

$$V_{N2} = \frac{-j\dfrac{1}{\omega C2}}{-j\dfrac{1}{\omega C1}-j\dfrac{1}{\omega C2}}6V\,p-p = \frac{C1}{C1+C2}6V\,p-p.$$

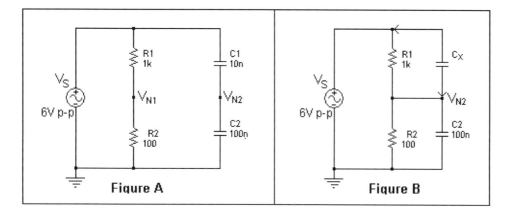

Figure A   Figure B

The voltage division is frequency independent. If both dividers divide by the same ratio, that is, $V_{N1} = V_{N2}$, then node N1 may be connected to node N2 without changing the voltage division ratio. This principle is used to "frequency compensate" oscilloscope probes.

An oscilloscope's input can be approximated as a resistance in parallel with a capacitance. The input impedance for a Tektronix TDS1002 is: 1 MΩ, ±2% in parallel with 20 pF, ±3pF.

In Figure B above, R2 and C2 could represent the oscilloscope input, and R1 and C_X could represent the probe.

Objectives

The characteristics of capacitive voltage dividers, and capacitive voltage dividers connected in parallel to resistive voltage dividers will be measured. The results will be compared to theoretical calculations.

Procedure

Equipment and Parts

Oscilloscope, Function Generator, and Breadboard.
Resistors: 100 Ω, 1 KΩ, all ¼ watt, 5%.
Capacitors: 10 nF, 20 nF (or 22 nF), 100 nF, all 5%.

---

1. Measure and record the values of your resistors and (if possible) capacitors.

    R1 _____   R2 _____   C2 _____

    C_X(10nF)_____ C_X(20nF)_____

2. Connect the circuit in Figure A on the previous page. Connect oscilloscope channel 1 to measure V_S, and channel 2 to node N1 to measure V_{N1}.

3. Set the function generator to produce a 6.00 V, peak-to-peak, sine wave with no offset, at a frequency of exactly 8.00 KHz. Use the oscilloscope to set the amplitude. This is the setting of the function generator for steps 4 through 7.

4. Measure and record the amplitude and phase angle of the voltage at node N1 with respect to V_S. Move the oscilloscope channel 2 to node N2. Measure and record the amplitude and phase angle of the voltage at node N2 with respect to V_S.

    V_{N1} _____ volts p-p θ_{N1} _____ degrees

    V_{N2} _____ volts p-p θ_{N2} _____ degrees

5. Connect the circuit in Figure B on the previous page without C_X. Connect the oscilloscope channel 1 to measure V_S (6.00 V peak-to-peak). Connect the oscilloscope channel 2 to node N2 to measure V_{N2}.

    V_{N2} _____ volts p-p θ_{N2} _____ degrees

6. Connect the circuit in Figure B with C_X = 10 nF. Connect the oscilloscope channel 2 to node N2 to measure V_{N2}.

    $V_{N2(10nF)}$ _____volts p-p $\theta_{N2(10nF)}$ _____ degrees

7. Connect the circuit in Figure B with C_X = 20 nF. Connect the oscilloscope channel 2 to node N2 to measure V_{N2}.

    $V_{N2(20nF)}$ _____ volts p-p $\theta_{N2(20nF)}$ _____ degrees

8. Connect the circuit in Figure B without C_X. Connect the oscilloscope channel 1 to observe V_S. Set the function generator to produce a 6.00 V, peak-to-peak, square wave with no offset, at a frequency of exactly 8.00 KHz. Use the oscilloscope to set the amplitude. This is the setting of the function generator for steps 9 through 11.

9. Connect channel 2 to node N2 to observe V_{N2}. Sketch or capture one cycle of the waveform on channel 2.

10. Connect the circuit in Figure B with $C_X = 10$ nF. Connect the oscilloscope channel 2 to node N2 to observe V_{N2}. Sketch or capture one cycle of the waveform on channel 2.

11. Connect the circuit in Figure B with $C_X = 20$ nF. Connect the oscilloscope channel 2 to node N2 to observe V_{N2}. Sketch or capture one cycle of the waveform on channel 2.

Analysis

1. Calculate the theoretical results for procedure steps 5 through 7 and compare the calculations to your measured results.

2. Use the specifications for the vertical input impedance of a Tektronix TDS1002 to design a compensated 10X probe (÷10). The cable connecting the probe to the vertical input adds 15 pF to the parallel capacitance. Calculate C_X and R_X in the model on right.

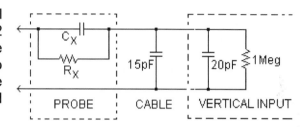

3. Optional: Compare your results in procedure steps 4 through 7 to a PSpice simulation. Use printers to obtain the magnitudes and phase angles of the voltages. See the example below.

All three situations are simulated simultaneously.

N1 is uncompensated.
N2 is compensated.
N3 is over compensated.

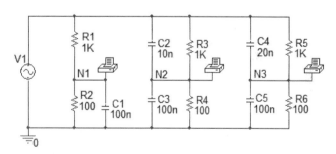

RESULTS AC ANALYSIS (From output file)	FREQ	VM(N1)	VP(N1)
	8.000E+03	4.961E-01	-2.456E+01
	FREQ	VM(N2)	VP(N2)
	8.000E+03	5.455E-01	-4.696E-15
	FREQ	VM(N3)	VP(N3)
	8.000E+03	6.782E-01	1.641E+01

4. Compare your results in procedure steps 9 through 11 to a PSpice simulation. Use Probe to obtain the response for each case.

[Replace the printers in step 3 above with voltage probes. Replace the AC source with a square wave source (Vpulse). Use transient analysis in the simulation settings.]

Experiment 23: Two-Source AC Circuit

Introduction

An AC circuit that is supplied by multiple sources of exactly the same frequency may be analyzed using the phasor method. A "voltage step down" transformer is used in this exercise to supply a circuit with two different voltages of the same frequency. Diagram A below shows a "text book" version of the circuit. Diagram B shows the actual circuit where the transformer provides about 9 V peak and 18 V peak at the power line frequency of 60 Hz. Compare the connections at nodes n1, n2, n3, and n4 in both diagrams.

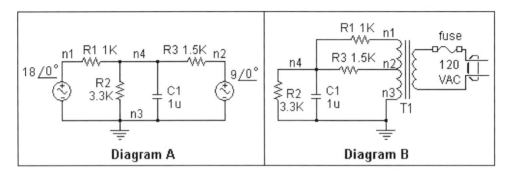

Objectives

The circuit voltage magnitude and phase measurements will be used to calculate the circuit currents. Node voltage and mesh current analysis will be used to compare the measured results to the theoretical calculations.

Procedure

> ### Equipment and Parts
>
> Transformer: 12.6 VAC center tapped, Oscilloscope, and Breadboard.
> Resistors: 1K, 1.5K, 3.3K, ¼ watt, 5%. Capacitor: 1 µF, non-polarized, 5%.

1. Measure and record the values of your resistors and capacitor.

    R1 _____   R2 _____   R3 _____   C1 _____

2. Connect the circuit in Diagram B above. Power the circuit.

3. Connect oscilloscope channel 1 to node n1 and channel 2 to node n2.

4. Measure and record the peak-to-peak values of the voltages at nodes n1 and n2. These voltages should be in phase.

    V1 _____ volts p-p   V2 _____volts p-p

5. Connect oscilloscope channel 2 to node n4.

6. Measure and record the peak-to-peak value of the voltage at node n4 and its phase angle with respect to V1.

    V4 _____ volts p-p   V4 _____ degrees

Analysis

1. Use the measured values of the voltages and the measured values of your components to calculate the voltage and phase angle of the voltage at node n4, V4. Use the node-voltage method to write the equation, and a scientific calculator, such as the TI-89, to solve the equation. See example below:

    csolve((x4-36)/1000+x4/3300+x4/(-2650i)+(x4-18)/1500=0,{x4})

    x4 = V4 = $(23.9 \angle 10.84^0)$

2. Simulate the circuit using the measured values of the voltages V1 and V2, and the measured values of your parts. Use transient analysis to generate a display of the voltages at the nodes, similar to the display on the right. Use the cursors to measure the peak-to-peak amplitude and phase angle of the voltage, V4.

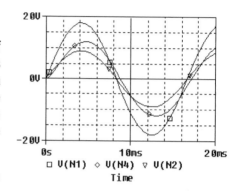

3. Verify that the simulated result for V4 is very close the calculated result.

4. Express the percent difference between the measured result and the calculated result for the voltage **V4**.

5. Calculate the impedance, **Z2**, of C1 and R2 in parallel. Use the mesh current method to calculate the currents **I1** and **I2**. Refer to the circuit on the right. Use the measured values of your components and the measured values of the voltages **V1** and **V2**.

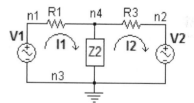

6. Calculate the voltage, **V4**, using the calculated currents, **I1** and **I2**. Compare the result of this calculation with the result of your analysis step 1.

TI-89 Mesh Current Example

Calculate the currents **I1** and **I2** and the voltage, **V4** in the circuit on the right using the mesh current method.

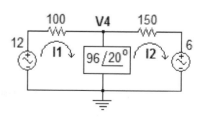

csolve(-12+100*x1+(96∠20)*x1-(96∠20)*x2=0 and
(96∠20)*x2-(96∠20)*x1+150*x2+6=0,{x1,x2})

x1 = **I1** = (61.12∠-7.52) mA   and   x2 = **I2** = (5.35∠94.3)mA

y4=((61.12∠-7.52)-(5.35∠94.3))*(96∠20)   y4 = **V4** = (5.99∠7.67)

91

Experiment 24: Thevenin's and Norton's Theorems

Introduction

Thevenin's and Norton's theorems are often used to simplify circuit analysis. They can also be used to find the impedance of a complex source. The Thevenin or Norton impedance of any source or circuit is equal to its Thevenin voltage divided by its Norton current (open circuit voltage divided by short circuit current).

The AC Thevenin voltage source has both a magnitude and phase angle. When connecting a Thevenin equivalent circuit the amplitude of the function generator can be set to the magnitude of the Thevenin equivalent voltage.

However, the <u>phase angle of the function generator can't be adjusted</u>. Therefore the Thevenin equivalent phase angle must be added to the measured phase angle in order to compare the Thevenin circuit phase angle to the original circuit phase angle.

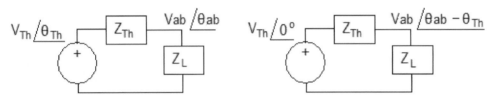

θab is the measured phase angle across Z_L with respect to Vs.

Objectives

This experiment will demonstrate the equivalence of a Thevenin circuit to the original circuit. The circuit's Thevenin voltage will be determined by measuring it's open circuit voltage. The circuit's Norton current will be determined by measuring its short circuit current. The circuit's Thevenin and Norton impedance will be calculated from the previous measurements.

Procedure

Equipment and Parts

Function Generator, Oscilloscope, and Breadboard.
R1 = 1.5K,   R2 = 1k, R_L = 1.8K, all ¼ watt, ±5%.
C = 100 nF, C_L = 47 nF, ±5%.

---

1.   Measure and record the values of R1, R2, R_L, and if possible, C, and C_L.

R1 _____   R2 _____ R_L _____

C _____ C_L _____

2. Connect the circuit in Figure A on the right.

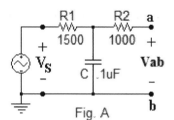

Fig. A

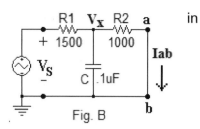

Fig. B

3. Connect oscilloscope channel 1 to measure V_S. Trigger on channel 1. Set the function generator, V_S, to produce an 8 V peak-to-peak, 1 KHz sine wave with no offset.

Note: The circuit in Figure A will be used to measure the circuit's open circuit voltage magnitude and phase angle. The circuit in Figure B will be used to measure the circuit's short circuit voltage magnitude and phase angle. Results will be used to calculate the circuit's Thevenin impedance.

Prepare a spreadsheet table to record your measurements:

	A	B	C	D	E	F	G
1	Load	Measured Vab - V p-p	Measured θab	Calculated Vab - V p-p	Calculated θab	% Error Vab - V p-p	% Error Degrees
3	Fig. A - None						
4	Fig. A - 1.8K						
5	Fig. A - 47nF						
6	Fig. C - None		*				
7	Fig. C - 1.8K		*				
8	Fig. C - 47nF		*				

* Add θTh to this measurement

4. Connect oscilloscope channel 2 to measure the magnitude and phase angle of the voltage **Vab.** Record the measurements into cells B3 and C3.

5. Connect a 1.8K resistor across terminals **a** and **b**. Vs must be 8 V peak-to-peak. Measure the magnitude and phase angle of the voltage **Vab** and record them in cells B4 and C4.

6. Connect a 47 nF capacitor across terminals **a** and **b**. Vs must be 8 V peak-to-peak. Measure the magnitude and phase angle of **Vab** and record into cells B5 and C5.

7. Connect a wire across the terminals **a** and **b** as shown in figure B. **Vs** must be 8 V peak-to-peak. Carefully measure and record the magnitude and phase of the voltage, V_X. Calculate and record the Thevenin impedance, Z_{Th}.

$V_{X(mag)}$ _____ $V_{X(phase)}$ _____

$Z_{Th(mag)}$ _____ $Z_{Th(phase)}$ _____

93

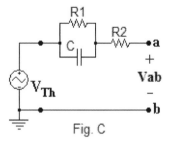

Fig. C

8.   Connect the circuit in Figure C on the right using the same components used in the circuit in Figure A (disassemble the circuit in Figure A).

Set the function generator to the voltage you measured in step 4 (cell B3). This is the circuit's Thevenin voltage, V_{TH}.

Since we can't set the phase angle of the function generator to the Thevenin equivalent phase angle, we will show that the phase angle of **Vab** for the Thevenin circuit is equal to the phase angle of the original circuit by adding the Thevenin phase angle to the measured phase angle.

The components are connected so that the impedance between the function generator and terminal **a** is equal to the Thevenin impedance.

9.   Connect channel 2 to measure the magnitude and phase angle of the voltage **Vab**. Record the measurements into cells B6 and C6.

10.   Connect a 1.8K resistor across terminals **a** and **b**. Make sure that V_{TH} is still equal to the voltage in cell B3. Measure the magnitude and phase angle of the voltage **Vab** and record into cells B7 and C7.

11.   Connect a 47 nF capacitor across terminals **a** and **b**. Make sure that V_{TH} is still equal to the voltage in cell B3. Measure the magnitude and phase angle of the voltage, **Vab** and record in cells B8 and C8.

PSpice Example: Thevenin Impedance

OrCAD PSpice may be used to determine the theoretical results. Use the measured values of your components for the simulation. The example here is used to obtain the circuit's open circuit voltage and short circuit current (Thevenin voltage and Norton current). The 10meg resistor, R3, simulates the input resistance of the oscilloscope.

FREQ	VM(A,0)	VP(A,0)
1.0E+03	5.82E+00	-4.33E+01

FREQ	IM(IPR.)	IP(IPR.)
1.0E+03	2.99E-03	-2.066E+01

Z_{Th} = (5.821 ∠ -43.3)/(2.994E-3 ∠ -20.66) = (1944 ∠ -22.64) ohms.

94

Analysis

1. Calculate the theoretical value of the Thevenin voltage, V_{Th}, and compare the result to that measured in step 4. Express differences in magnitude and phase as percents.

2. Calculate the theoretical value of the Norton current, I_N, and compare the result to that measured in step 7. Use V_X to calculate the measured value of I_N. ($I_N = V_X/R2$). Express differences in magnitude and phase as percents.

3. Calculate the value of the Thevenin impedance using the results of analysis steps 1 and 2 above.

4. Calculate the theoretical value of the Thevenin impedance using the values of the resistors and the reactance of the capacitor. This result should be the same as the results of your calculations in analysis step 3.

5. Complete the spreadsheet table in step 3 of the procedure.

   You can use the calculator or simulation for columns D and E, and the spreadsheet to calculate columns F and G.

   Columns F and G in the table on page 93 express the error in the voltage and phase angle measurements when compared to the theoretical calculations.

PSpice Example: 1.8K Load

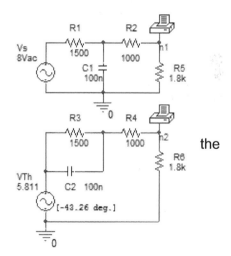

FREQ	VM(N1)	VP(N1)
1.000E+03	2.854E+00	-3.154E+01

FREQ	VM(N2)	VP(N2)
1.000E+03	2.849E+00	1.177E+01

Note that adding the -43.26 degree phase angle of Thevenin source to VP(N2) results in the phase angle of -31.49 degrees, which is in close agreement to the result for the original circuit.

the

95

Experiment 25: Audio Output Transformer

Introduction

The voltage, current, and impedance transformation equations for an ideal transformer are given below.

$$\frac{V_P}{V_S} = \frac{N_P}{N_S} \qquad \frac{I_P}{I_S} = \frac{N_S}{N_P} \qquad \left(\frac{Z_P}{Z_S} = \frac{N_P}{N_S}\right)^2$$

An AC voltage source with a source impedance of 1000 Ω is first connected directly to an 8.2 Ω resistor, and the power delivered to it is measured. Then the same load resistance is connected to the source through an impedance matching transformer, and the power delivered to the 8.2 Ω resistor is again measured. In addition, the primary and secondary voltages and currents will be determined and compared to the voltage transformation properties of the transformer.

An audio output transformer is used which is designed to match a high impedance audio amplifier output to a low impedance loudspeaker. An 8 Ω loudspeaker will replace the 8.2 Ω resistor, and the measurements will be repeated. This will also provide an audible demonstration of the effectiveness of the transformer.

In the second part of this exercise the transformer primary will be connected as an "auto-transformer", and its voltage and impedance matching properties will be explored.

Objectives

This lab experiment demonstrates that the voltage, current, and impedance transformation properties of an iron core transformer approximate that of an ideal transformer.

Procedure

Equipment and Parts
Function Generator, Oscilloscope, DMM, and Breadboard. Audio Transformer, 1000 Ω, center tapped, to 8 Ω, 200 mW. Loudspeaker, 8 Ω, 200 mW minimum, (2 to 4 inch). Resistors: R1: 8.2, R2: 1000, R3: 220, R4: 47, R5: 470, all ¼ watt, 5%.

Part 1: Impedance Transformation

1.   Measure the values of the resistors for use in your analysis.

R1 _____   R2 _____   R3 _____

R4 _____   R5 _____

2. Connect the circuit on the right. Connect channel 1 of the oscilloscope to Vg, the function generator. Connect channel 2 of the oscilloscope to measure Vo.

    Set the oscilloscope to trigger on channel 1. Set the function generator to produce a 10 V peak-to-peak, 1000Hz sine wave with no offset.

3. Measure and record the magnitude and phase of the voltage Vo.

    Vo(mag) _____ V p-p   Vo(angle) _____ Degrees

4. Connect the circuit on the right. Connect channel 1 of the oscilloscope to Vg, the function generator. Connect channel 2 of the oscilloscope to measure Vo.

    Set the oscilloscope to trigger on channel 1. Set the function generator to produce a 10 V peak-to-peak, 1000 Hz sine wave with no offset.

5. Measure and record the magnitude and phase of the voltage Vo.

    Vo(mag) _____ volts p-p.   Vo(angle) _____ degrees.

6. Measure and record the magnitude and phase of the voltage Vp.

    Vp(mag) _____ volts p-p.   Vp(angle) _____ degrees.

7. Measure and record the resistance of the loudspeaker. Sp _____ohms.

8. Connect the circuit on the right. Connect channel 1 of the oscilloscope to Vg, the function generator. Connect channel 2 of the oscilloscope to measure Vo.

    Set the oscilloscope to trigger on channel 1. Set the function generator to produce a 10 V peak-to-peak, 1000 Hz sine wave with no offset.

9. Measure and record the magnitude and phase of Vo.

    Vo(mag) _____ volts p-p.   Vo(angle) _____ degrees.

10. Connect the circuit on the right. Connect channel 1 of the oscilloscope to Vg, the function generator. Connect channel 2 of the oscilloscope to measure Vo.

    Set the oscilloscope to trigger on channel 1. Set the function generator to produce a 10 V peak-to-peak, 1000 Hz sine wave with no offset.

11.   Measure and record the magnitude and phase of Vo.

        Vo(mag) _____ volts p-p.   Vo(angle) _____ degrees.

12.   Measure and record the magnitude and phase of the voltage Vp.

        Vp(mag) _____ volts p-p.   Vp(angle): _____ degrees.

Part 2: Autotransformer

1.   Connect the circuit on the right with R_L = 47 Ω. Connect
        channel 1 of the oscilloscope to Vg, the function generator.
        Connect channel 2 of the oscilloscope to measure Vo.

        Set the oscilloscope to trigger on channel 1. Set the function
        generator to produce a 10 V peak-to-peak, 1000 Hz sine
        wave with no offset.

2.   Measure and record the magnitude and phase of the voltage Vo.

        Vo(mag) _____ volts p-p.   Vo(angle) _____ degrees.

3.   Measure and record the magnitude and phase of the voltage Vp.

        Vp(mag) _____ volts p-p.   Vp(angle) _____ degrees.

4.   Repeat step 1 with R_L = 220 Ω.

5.   Measure and record the magnitude and phase of the voltage Vo.

        Vo(mag) _____ volts p-p.   Vo(angle) _____ degrees.

6.   Measure and record the magnitude and phase of the voltage Vp.

        Vp(mag) _____ volts p-p.   Vp(angle) _____ degrees.

7.   Repeat step 1 with R_L = 470 Ω.

8.   Measure and record the magnitude and phase of the voltage Vo.

        Vo(mag) _____ volts p-p.   Vo(angle) _____ degrees.

9.   Measure and record the magnitude and phase of the voltage Vp.

        Vp(mag) _____ volts p-p.   Vp(angle) _____ degrees.

Analysis, Part 1

1. Use the measurements in step 3 to calculate power delivered to the 8.2 Ω load resistor. Compare measured power to the theoretically expected power. Calculate the ratio of the power delivered to the load resistor to the power delivered by the source.

2. Use the measurements in step 5 to calculate power delivered to the 8.2 Ω load resistor. Compare measured to theoretically expected power. Calculate the ratio of load resistor power to power delivered by the source (also use results of step 6).

3. Use the measurements in steps 5 and 6 to calculate the voltage and current transformation ratios of the transformer, and compare the measured values to the theoretically expected values.

4. Explain the results for the phase angles between the source, Vg, and the voltages Vp and Vo in steps 5 and 6.

5. Optional and challenging: Refer to the circuit on the right. Measure the inductance, Lp and Ls, and resistance, Rp and Rs, of the primary and secondary windings. Calculate the voltage, Vo, across the 8.2 ohm load resistor by including the transformer's winding resistances, Rp and Rs.

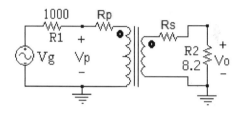

Use the mesh current method and assume a coupling coefficient of 0.95. Compare your calculated results to your measured results

Analysis, Part 2

1. Use the measurements in part 2, steps 2 and 3, to calculate the power delivered to 47 Ω load resistor. Compare the measured power to the theoretically expected power. Calculate the ratio of the power delivered to the load resistor to the power delivered by the source.

2. Use the measurements in part 2, steps 5 and 6, to calculate the power delivered to 220 Ω load resistor. Compare the measured power to the theoretically expected power. Calculate the ratio of the power delivered to the load resistor to the power delivered by the source.

3. Use the measurements in part 2, steps 8 and 9, to calculate the power delivered to 470 Ω load resistor. Compare the measured power to the theoretically expected power. Calculate the ratio of the power delivered to the load resistor to the power delivered by the source.

4. Compare and comment on the results of the ratio of power delivered to the load resistor to the power delivered by the source for the 47 Ω, 220 Ω, and 470 Ω load resistors.

Transformer Simulation Notes

You need to approximate the inductance of the primary winding (300 mH was used in this simulation). The secondary inductance is calculated from the turns ratio which is equal to the square root of the inductance ratio.

See the simulation of this lab exercise below.

Part 1: LTspice

In LTspice, a transformer is modeled with coupled inductors with a mutual inductance statement placed as a SPICE directive on the schematic. The diagram below includes the directive: K1 L1 L2 1. K1 is the coupling coefficient between L1 and L2 and is set to 1. Inductors must have a phasing dot.

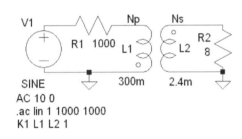

```
--- AC Analysis ---

frequency: 1000 Hz
V(np):    mag:    4.83287   phase:   14.8561°
V(ns):    mag:    0.432265  phase: -165.144°
V(n001)   mag:         10   phase:        0°
I(R2):    mag:  0.0540331   phase: -165.144°
I(R1):    mag: 0.00547085   phase:  166.909°
I(V1):    mag: 0.00547085   phase:  166.909°
```

Part 2: PSpice / Auto-transformer.

The evaluation version of PSpice has the linear transformer, XFRM_LINEAR, that can be used to simulate this lab. Double click on the transformer to open the property editor. There are three parameters that can be set for the simulation: COUPLING, L1_VALUE, and L2_VALUE.

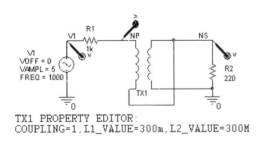

TX1 PROPERTY EDITOR:
COUPLING=1, L1_VALUE=300m, L2_VALUE=300M

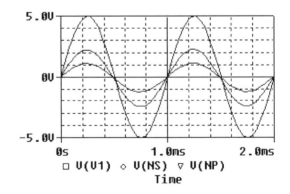

Experiment 26: AC Power Basics

Introduction

This experiment illustrates the relationship between average power, reactive power, and apparent power.

Fig. 1 on the right shows the phasor diagram for a series RC circuit where the capacitive reactance is equal to the inductive reactance. The resistor and capacitor voltages are equal but 90 degrees out of phase.

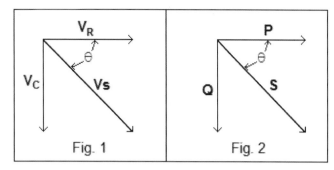

Fig. 1   Fig. 2

Fig. 2 shows the phasor diagram for the circuit power. **P** is the power consumed by the resistor, **Q** is the reactive power of the capacitor, and **S** is the apparent power supplied to the circuit. Note that the angles for the component power correspond to the angles for the component voltage. For this correspondence to be true, the apparent power **S** is calculated as the product of the applied voltage times the complex conjugate of the circuit current: $\mathbf{S} = \mathbf{V} \mathbf{I}^{*}$.

Note: $\mathbf{V_R} = |\mathbf{Vs}|\cos\theta$ and $\mathbf{P} = |\mathbf{S}|\cos\theta$. $\mathbf{V_C} = j|\mathbf{Vs}|\sin\theta$ and $\mathbf{Q} = j|\mathbf{S}|\sin\theta$

Objectives

The voltage magnitudes and phase angles across the resistor and capacitor in a series RC circuit will be measured. Resistor and capacitor power, P and Q, will be calculated from these measurements. The power relationship in the series RC circuit will be investigated and compared to theoretical calculations.

Procedure

Equipment and Parts

Function Generator, Oscilloscope, DMM, and Breadboard.
Resistor: 1000-ohm, ¼ watt, 5%. Capacitor: 100nF, 5%.

1.   Measure the value of the resistor:

      R _____

2.   Connect the circuit in Figure A.
      Vs is the function generator. Connect channel 1 of the oscilloscope to node n1 and channel 2 to node n2.

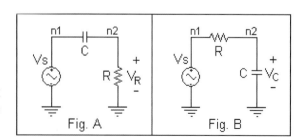

Fig. A   Fig. B

3.   Set the function generator to produce a 1600 Hz, 10 V peak-to-peak, sine wave.

4.   Measure and record the peak-to-peak voltage V_R at node n2.

      $V_{R\ mag}$ _____ volts peak-to-peak.

5.   Measure and record the phase angle of the voltage V_R at node n2 with respect to the voltage Vs at node n1.

      $V_{R\ Phase}$ _____ degrees. Leading or lagging?

6.   Set the DMM to measure AC volts. Measure and record the voltage Vs at node n1 and V_R at node n2 with the DMM.

      DMM Measurement: Vs _____ volts rms. V_R _____ volts rms.

      Does the measurement of the magnitude of V_R agree with the oscilloscope measurement of V_R in step 4. Check that:

$$V_R(\text{step}\,4)=2\sqrt{2}\,V_R(\text{step}\,5),\ \text{within about 2\%.}$$

7.   Connect the circuit in Figure B. Vs is the function generator.   Connect channel 1 of the oscilloscope to node n1 and channel 2 to node n2. Do not change the function generator amplitude and frequency.   The amplitude should be 10 V peak-to-peak and the frequency should be 1600 Hz.

8.   Measure and record the peak-to-peak voltage V_C at node n2.

      V_C _____ volts peak-to-peak.

9.   Measure and record the phase angle of the voltage V_C at node n2 with respect to the voltage Vs at node n1.

      $V_{C\ Phase}$ _____ degrees. Leading or lagging?

10.   Set the DMM to measure AC volts. Measure and record the voltage Vs at node n1 and the voltage V_C at node n2 with the DMM.

      DMM Measurement: Vs _____ volts rms. V_C _____ volts rms.

Analysis

1.   Note that the purpose of the two circuits was to be able to measure the resistor voltage and the capacitor voltage with respect to the common grounds of the function generator and oscilloscope.

      Both circuits have the same impedance and therefore the same current. The current can be calculated using the voltage measured across the resistor in step 4 and Ohm's Law. $I = V_R/R$.

Calculate and record peak-to-peak magnitude of **I** in mA and the phase angle of **I** in degrees using the voltage and phase angle of V_R measured in steps 4 and 5 of the procedure. <u>This is the measured current in because it is calculated from the measured voltage.</u>

I _____mA peak to peak. **I** Phase _____ degrees.

2. Convert the magnitude of **I** to RMS units.

I _____mA RMS

3. Calculate and record the apparent power, **S**, supplied to the circuit by the source, **Vs**. Use the measured current from analysis step 2. Express the result in mVA and in polar form (magnitude and phase angle).

S _____mVA   (Measured apparent power).

4. Calculate and record the average power, P, and the reactive power, Q_C by expressing the value of **S** in step 3 above in rectangular form.
P _____mW Q_C _____mVAR.

5. Calculate P and Q_C using values measured by the DMM in procedure steps 6 and 10. Compare the result to the analysis step 4 result. Although the DMM does not measure phase angle, the results of procedure step 4 (oscilloscope measurements) and procedure step 6 (DMM measurements) should be in close agreement.

6. Calculate the theoretical value of the apparent power, **S**.   Compare the result to the oscilloscope measurement result of analysis step 3 above. Express the percent difference between the theoretical and measured results for the power dissipated by the resistor for the reactive power of the capacitor.

7. Optional: Simulate the circuit and compare the results to your calculations and measurements.

LTspice Example

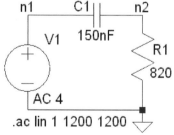

```
--- AC Analysis ---

frequency: 1200 Hz
V(n2):      mag:     2.71996 phase: 47.1572°
V(n1):      mag:           4 phase:       0°
I(R1):      mag: 0.00331702 phase: 47.1572°
```

Source voltage, Vs, is 4.0-volts rms.

$$S = VsI^* = 4(.003317\angle -47.16^0) = 13.27\,mVA = 9.02 - j9.73\,mVA$$

P=9.02mW dissipated.   Q=9.73mVARs capacitive.

Experiment 27: Power Factor Compensation / Parallel Circuit

Introduction

This experiment demonstrates power factor compensation of a load using a parallel connected compensation component. The circuit block diagram below shows a voltage source, V_S, with internal resistance, R_S, connected to a load whose apparent power is $S_1 + S_2$.

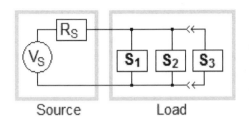

Source   Load

Power factor compensation of the load is accomplished by connecting a component in parallel with the load so that its reactive VARs, S_3, cancel the reactive VARs of $S_1 + S_2$.

That is: $S_{Load} = S_1 + S_2 + S_3 = P$.

In this experiment the source resistance is 1000 ohms. The load is a 1000 ohm resistor connected in parallel with an inductor. The compensation component will be a capacitor.

Objectives

Voltages in a series-parallel RL circuit will be measured. The power associated with the inductor and the resistors will be calculated from the voltage measurements. A compensating capacitor will be connected to the circuit and the compensated circuit will be compared to the uncompensated one.

Procedure

Equipment and Parts
Function Generator, Oscilloscope, and Breadboard.
Resistors: Two 1K, ¼ W, 5%. Inductor: 100 mH, 5%. Capacitor: 100 nF, 5%.

1. Measure the value of each resistor, the resistance of the inductor, R_1 and if possible, the values of the inductance, L_1 and capacitance, C.

    R_S _____ R_1 _____ R_2 _____

    L_1 _____   C __103 nF__

2. Connect the circuit on the right <u>without the capacitor</u>, C. This connection will be referred to as the "uncompensated" circuit.

3. Connect oscilloscope channel 1 to measure **V1** and oscilloscope channel 2 to measure **V2**. Set the trigger to channel 1.

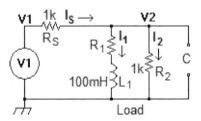

104

4. Set the function generator, **V1**, to produce a 6 V peak-to-peak,1600 Hz sine wave with no offset. Set channels 1 and 2 of the oscilloscope to get a display similar to that shown below.

Both traces are centered vertically and the reference voltage, **V1**, crosses zero at the horizontal center of the screen.

The TDS1002 is used to measure the amplitudes of **V1** and **V2**.

V2 crosses zero volts about 44 microseconds before **V1**. It is leading **V1** so its angle is positive:

$$\text{Angle} = \frac{44}{625}\,360 = 25.34\,\text{Degrees}$$

The oscilloscope's time base should be adjusted to measure the time difference between the zero crossings of **V1** and **V2** most accurately.

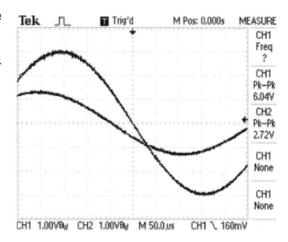

5. Set up a spreadsheet as shown below:

	A	B	C	D	E	F	G	H	I	J
1	Circuit	Freq.	T mSec	t mSec	V2 Mag	V2 Deg	I mA	I Deg	P mW	Ps mW
3	Un-comp	1600	0.625							
4	Comp	1600	0.625							

6. Measure the peak-to-peak amplitude of **V2** and enter the value into spreadsheet cell E3. Measure the time difference between the zero crossings of **V1** and **V2**.

If available, use "cursors" to measure the time difference. Record the results into spreadsheet cell D3. The time difference is positive if **V2** crosses zero before **V1**, and negative if **V2** crosses zero after **V1**.

7. Connect the 0.1μF compensating capacitor, C1, into the circuit. Check that the generator's output is still 6 V peak-to-peak.

Measure the magnitude of **V2** and enter the value into spreadsheet cell E4.

Measure the time difference between the zero crossings of **V1** and **V2**. Record the results into spreadsheet cell D4.

Analysis

1. Calculate the values for columns F through J of the spreadsheet using the measurements in columns C, D, and E. The angle of V2 in column F may be calculated by the spreadsheet. Enter into cell F3: =(D3/C3)*360.

    The current I in column G is calculated: $I = \dfrac{6\angle 0 - V2\angle \theta 2}{R1}$.

    Enter result into spreadsheet cells G and H. Enter current in mA units.

2. Show that the 100 nF capacitor is approximately the required capacitor value to compensate the circuit at 1600 Hz.

3. Calculate the power P delivered to the load resistor, R2, and the power supplied by the source, Ps, for the uncompensated and compensated circuits.

    Record the results in the appropriate cells, I, and J. You can input the equations below into cells, I3, and J3 to let the spreadsheet do the calculations.

    P = 1000*V2*V2/(8*R2) mW   Cell I3: =1000*E3*E3/(8*R2) mW

    Ps = 6*I*cos(V2 Deg)/8   Cell J3: =(6*G3*cos(H3*3.14/180))/8

    Ps is in mW because I is in mA. The factor ÷8 converts p-p to rms.

4. Calculate the percent efficiency of the compensated and uncompensated circuit in delivering power to R2. %Eff = (P/Ps) X 100%.

5. Simulate the circuit using AC sweep analysis. Printer (VPRINT1) at node N2.

    Set the sweep to "LIN" and the start and stop frequencies to 1600 Hz.

    Use your measured component values. See example on the right.

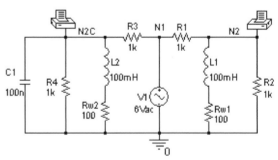

6. Calculate the percent difference between the simulated results and the measured results for the magnitude and phase angle of V2 for the compensated circuit at 1600Hz..

7. Explain why the compensated circuit delivers more power to the load (R2) than the uncompensated one.

8. Calculate the theoretical power factor of the uncompensated and of the compensated circuit at 1600 Hz. Calculate the power factor of the uncompensated and of the compensated circuit at 1600 Hz, using the measured voltages at node N2. Compare the results.

Experiment 28: Series Compensation and Power Transfer

Introduction

Electrical power is delivered to loads by means of wire transmission lines. Long transmission lines also have a significant inductive and capacitive reactance. The voltage developed across the resistance and reactance of a transmission line reduces the voltage and power supplied to the load. A capacitor placed in series with a transmission line may be used to compensate for the line's inductance.

Capacitance in series with an inductive transmission can be used to increase the power delivered to the load. Power transmission is improved by making the reactance of the capacitor equal to the inductance of the transmission line. The net reactance for inductance and capacitance in series is: $X = j(X_L - X_C)$.

Recall that the maximum power transfer theorem for AC states that maximum power transfer occurs when the load impedance is equal to the complex conjugate of the source impedance.

Objectives

In this experiment the load is a 330 Ω resistor. A 100 mH inductor simulates the transmission line inductance and resistance. A compensating capacitor will be placed in series with the inductor. This exercise will show that much more power is delivered to the load by the compensated transmission line.

Procedure

Equipment and Parts

Function Generator, Oscilloscope, and Breadboard.
Resistor: 330 Ω, ¼ W, 5%. Inductor: 100 mH, 5%. Capacitor: 100 nF, 5%.

---

1. Measure the value of the resistor, the resistance of the inductor, and if possible, the inductance of the inductor and capacitance of the capacitor.

   R2 _____   R_W _____   L1 _____   C1 _____

2. Connect the circuit on the right with a jumper wire across the capacitor. This will be the uncompensated circuit <u>without the capacitor</u>, C1.

3. Set the generator, V1, to produce a 12 V peak-to-peak, 1600 Hz sine wave at node N1, as measured by the oscilloscope channel 1.

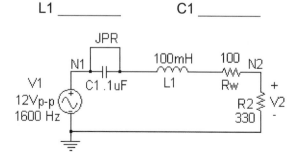

4.   Set up a spreadsheet for your measurements as shown below:

	A	B	C	D	E	F	G	H	I	J
1	Circuit	Freq	T mS	t mS	V2 Mag	V2 Deg	I mA	I Deg	P mW	Pin mW
3	Uncomp.	1600	0.625							
4	Comp	1600	0.625							
5	Comp*	800	1.25							
6	Comp*	3200	0.3125							

Note: Columns F through K will be calculated by the spreadsheet. Instructions for the calculations are given in the analysis section of this lab exercise.

5.   Connect channel 2 of the oscilloscope to node N2. Measure the peak-to-peak value of the voltage V2, at node N2, and record in cell E3. Measure the time interval in milliseconds between the zero crossings of V2 and V1 and record in cell D3. If V2 crosses at a later time than V1, record the time as negative.

6.   Remove the jumper wire across the capacitor. This will now be the compensated circuit <u>with the capacitor</u>, C1.

7.   Set the function generator to produce a 12.0 V peak-to-peak, 1600 Hz sine wave at node N1, as measured by the oscilloscope channel 1.

8.   Connect channel 2 of the oscilloscope to node N2. Measure the peak-to-peak value of the voltage V2, at node N2, and record in cell E4. Measure the time interval in milliseconds between the zero crossings of V2 and V1 and record in cell D4.

9.   Set the function generator to produce a 12.0 V peak-to-peak, 800 Hz sine wave, V1, at node N1, as measured by the oscilloscope channel 1.

10.   Connect channel 2 of the oscilloscope to node N2. Measure the peak-to-peak value of the voltage V2, at node N2, and record in cell E5. Measure the time interval in milliseconds between the zero crossings of V2 and V1, and record in cell D5.

11.   Set the function generator to produce a 12.0 V peak-to-peak, 3200 Hz sine wave, V1, at node N1, as measured by the oscilloscope channel 1.

12.   Connect channel 2 of the oscilloscope to node N2. Measure the peak-to-peak value of the voltage V2, at node N2, and record in cell E6. Measure the time interval in milliseconds between the zero crossings of V2 and V1, and record in cell D6.

Analysis

1.   Verify the following equations and enter them into the indicated cells:

<u>Cell F3</u> =(D3/C3)*360   <u>Cell G3</u> =1000*E3/R2   <u>Cell H3</u> =F3

<u>Cell I3</u> =1000*(E3*E3)/(8*R2)   <u>Cell J3</u> =(12*G3*cos(H3*3.14/180))/8

108

2. Use the "fill down" feature of the spreadsheet to calculate the results for each spreadsheet column rows 4 through 6.

The example spreadsheet below was produced using PSpice simulation data and the labeled values of capacitance and inductance. Your results should be within about 20% of those in the spreadsheet below.

	A	B	C	D	E	F	G	H	I	J
1	Circuit	Freq	T mS	t mS	V2 Mag	V2 Deg	I mA	I Deg	P mW	Pin mW
3	Uncomp	1600	0.6250	-0.116	3.62	-66.8	10.97	-66.8	4.96	6.49
4	Comp	1600	0.6250	-0.002	9.21	-1.4	27.91	-1.4	32.13	41.85
5	Comp*	800	1.2500	0.256	2.56	73.7	7.76	73.7	2.48	3.27
6	Comp*	3200	0.3125	-0.065	2.52	-74.9	7.64	-74.9	2.41	3.00

3. Simulate the circuit with AC sweep analysis and a printer (VPRINT1) at node N2. Set the sweep to "LOG" and "OCTAVE" and use one point per octave. Be sure to use your measured component values.

PSpice Simulation Example:

Compensated

FREQ	VM(N2C)	VP(N2C)
8.000E+02	2.559E+00	7.387E+01
1.600E+03	9.207E+00	-1.411E+00
3.200E+03	2.517E+00	-7.414E+01

Uncompensated

FREQ	VM(N2)	VP(N2)
8.000E+02	5.987E+00	-4.945E+01
1.600E+03	3.622E+00	-6.684E+01
3.200E+03	1.926E+00	-7.793E+01

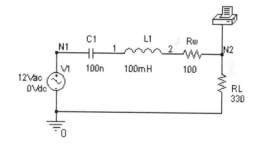

4. Calculate the percent difference between the simulated results and the measured results for the magnitude and phase angle of V2.

5. Explain why the compensated circuit delivers more power to the load (R2) than the uncompensated one at 1600Hz.

6. Explain the results of your measurements at 800Hz and 3200Hz.

Useful Equations are presented below. Voltages and currents must be in RMS units.

$$|\mathbf{S}|=|\mathbf{Vs}||\mathbf{Is}| \qquad P=|Is|^2 \, RL + |Is|^2 \, (Rw) \qquad \mathbf{pf}=\frac{P}{|\mathbf{S}|}=\cos\theta \qquad P_{LOAD}=|Is|^2\,(RL)$$

Experiment 29: Three-Phase Power / Wye Connection

Introduction

This lab exercise uses the "Phase Tripler" circuit described in appendix 2 of this manual. It is a 3-phase wye source with an ACB phase sequence. The neutral connection of this source shares the same ground as the lab power supply, function generator, and oscilloscope. Therefore care must be taken to not ground a phase output, such as would occur if the ground lead of the oscilloscope were connected to one of the phase outputs. Study the diagram of a typical 120 VAC power system below. The grounds of the oscilloscope and function generator are connected together through the AC receptacle.

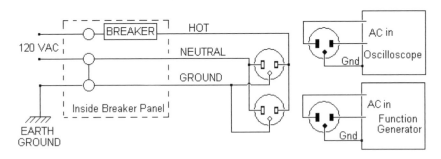

Note that the wide connector on the receptacle and the ground connector are connected together and to earth ground at the breaker panel. So the function generator and oscilloscope grounds are connected together through the AC power outlets.

Objectives

This exercise involves the measurement of the magnitude and phase of voltages and currents in a 4-wire, 3-phase, wye connected power system. The effect of balanced and unbalanced loads with and without the neutral wire will be measured.

Procedure

Equipment and Parts

Function Generator, Power Supply, Phase Tripler Board, Oscilloscope, and Breadboard. Resistors: Four 100 Ω, Three 390 Ω, 220 Ω, ¼ watt, 5%.

Do not measure the values of the components. Use components that have a five percent or better tolerance rating.

Part 1: Balanced Load

Before starting this exercise, read the "Phase Tripler Circuit Information" in Appendix 2. If you don't have the phase tripler board, one could be built on a breadboard using the schematic diagram and calibration procedure provided. The Phase Tripler printed circuit board is available from: www.zapstudio.com.

1. Connect the Phase Tripler Board to the power supplies and function generator as shown on the right.

   Set the power supply to +12VDC and −12VDC. Set the generator to produce a 60Hz, 12 V peak-to-peak, sine wave.

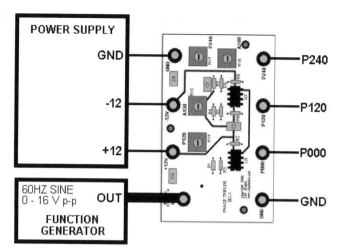

2. Connect channel 1 of the oscilloscope to P000 and set the trigger to channel 1. Set the function generator amplitude to get exactly 12 V peak-to-peak on channel 1.

3. Connect channel 2 of the oscilloscope to P120. Check that the amplitude is exactly 12 V peak-to-peak and that the phase is leading channel 1 by exactly 120^0.

4. Connect channel 2 of the oscilloscope to P240. Check that the amplitude is exactly 12 V peak-to-peak and that the phase is lagging channel 1 by exactly 120^0.

   [Refer to the calibration procedure in Appendix 2 if steps 3 and 4 don't check.]

5. Connect the Phase Tripler Board to a wye load as shown on the right.

6. Connect the oscilloscope to P000. The ground must be connected to the phase tripler ground for this entire lab. Channel 1 is the zero degree phase reference for all measurements made with channel 2.

7. Measure the magnitude and phase of the voltages at nodes nG, nA, nB, and nC with channel 2. Record results below.

Step 7 node	nG	nA	nB	nC
Magnitude p-p				
Phase, Deg.				

8. Open the neutral line by removing the 100-ohm resistor between the phase tripler ground and node nG.

9. Measure the magnitude and phase angle of the voltages at nodes nG, nA, nB, and nC with the oscilloscope channel 2 and record results in the table below.

Step 9 node	nG	nA	nB	nC
Magnitude p-p				
Phase, Deg.				

Part 2: Unbalanced Load

1. Replace RC with a 220 Ω resistor and reconnect the 100 Ω resistor between node Ng and COMMON as shown on the right.

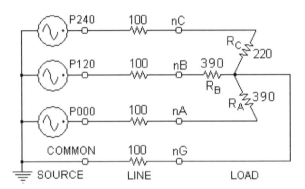

2. Measure the magnitude and phase angle of the voltages at nodes nG, nA, nB, and nC with the oscilloscope channel 2 and record results in the table below.

Step 2 node	nG	nA	nB	nC
Magnitude p-p				
Phase, Deg.				

3. Open the neutral line by removing the 100 Ω resistor between the phase tripler ground and node nG.

4. Measure the magnitude and phase angle of the voltages at nodes nG, nA, nB, and nC with the oscilloscope channel 2 and record results in the table below.

Step 4 node	nG	nA	nB	nC
Magnitude p-p				
Phase, Deg.				

Analysis, Part 1

1. Use the node voltage method to calculate the voltage at node nG. Use the result to calculate the current supplied by the source for each phase.

2. Calculate the voltages at nodes nA, nB, and nC. Calculate the neutral wire current.

112

3.   Calculate the percent difference between the measured and calculated values of the voltages at nodes nA, nB, and nC.

Analysis, Part 2

1.   Use PSpice to simulate the unbalanced circuit with and without the neutral connection. Refer to the example below. Include the part "IPRINT" in series with each source and the neutral wire to measure the magnitude and phase angle of the current for each phase and for the neutral wire.

2.   Calculate the percent difference between the measured and simulated values of the voltages at nodes nA, nB, and nC.

3.   Use Kirchhoff's current law to show that the neutral wire current is the result of the unbalance of the phase currents.

PSpice 3 Phase Analysis

Three phase circuits can be simulated using three "VAC" sources from the source library.

Double click on each source to open its property editor to set its phase angle. Click on "Display" and set each to display its name and value.

See the schematic diagram on the right and the edited simulation results below for a balanced and unbalanced load.

Use "AC Sweep analysis" with the start and end frequencies set to 60 Hertz and the number of points set to 1.

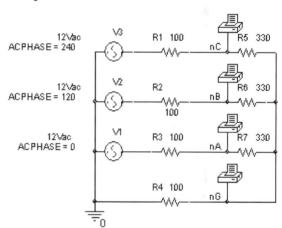

The last two columns show the results when the load is unbalanced by replacing one of the 330 Ω resistors with a 1000 Ω resistor.

60 Hertz	R5=330, R6=330, R7=330.			R5=1K, R6=330, R7=330.	
Node	Mag V p-p	Phase Deg.		Mag V p-p	Phase Deg.
nC	9.209	-120		10.081	-120
nB	9.209	120		9.339	118.7
nA	9.209	0		9.339	1.35
nG	0	N.A.		1.092	60.0

Experiment 30: Three Phase Power / Delta Connection

Introduction

This lab exercise uses the "Phase Tripler" circuit described in appendix 2 in this manual. It is a 3-phase wye source with an ACB phase sequence. The neutral connection of this source shares the same ground as the lab power supply, function generator, and oscilloscope. Therefore care must be taken to not ground a phase output, such as would occur if the ground lead of the oscilloscope were connected to one of the phase outputs.

Objectives

This exercise involves the measurement of the magnitude and phase of voltages and currents in a 3-wire, 3-phase, delta connected power system. The effect of balanced and unbalanced loads is measured.

Procedure

Equipment and Parts

Function Generator, Power Supply, Phase Tripler Board, Oscilloscope, and Breadboard.
Resistors: 220-ohm, Three 390-ohm, ¼ watt, 5%.
Inductors: Three 100mH, 5% (iron core, 50mA minimum).

Don"t measure the values of the components. Use components with a 5% or better accuracy.

Before starting this exercise, read the "Phase Tripler Circuit Information" in appendix 2 of this manual. If you don't have the phase tripler board, one could be built on a breadboard using the schematic diagram and calibration procedure provided. The Phase Tripler printed circuit board is available at: www.zapstudio.com.

1.   Connect the phase tripler board to the power supplies and function generator as shown on the right. Set the power supply to +12VDC and –12VDC. Set the generator to produce a 60 Hz, 12 V peak-to-peak, sine wave.

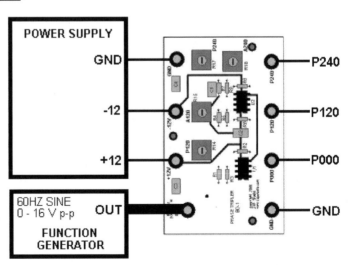

2.   Connect channel 1 of the oscilloscope to P000 and set trigger to channel 1. Set the function generator amplitude to get exactly 12 V peak-to-peak on channel 1.

3. Connect channel 2 to P120. Check that the amplitude is exactly 12 V peak-to-peak and that the phase is leading channel 1 by exactly 120^0.

4. Connect channel 2 to P240. Check that the amplitude is exactly 12 V peak-to-peak and that the phase is lagging channel 1 by exactly 120^0.

   [Refer to the calibration procedure in Appendix 2 if steps 3 and 4 don't check.]

5. Connect the phase tripler source to the load as shown on the right.

6. Connect the oscilloscope to P000. The ground must be connected to the phase tripler ground and never anywhere else for this entire lab. Channel 1 will be the zero degree phase reference for measurements made with channel 2.

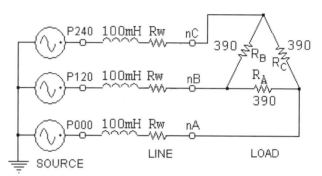

7. Measure the magnitude and phase angle of the voltages at nodes nA, nB, and nC with the oscilloscope channel 2 and record results in the table below (balanced case).

Step 7 node	nA	nB	nC
Magnitude p-p	11.6	10.4	11.2
Phase, Deg.			

⊗ Use equations on next page

8. Replace the 390 Ω resistor R_C with a 220 Ω resistor.

9. Measure the magnitude and phase angle of the voltages at nodes nA, nB, and nC with the oscilloscope channel 2 and record results in the table below (unbalanced case).

Step 9 node	nA	nB	nC
Magnitude p-p	12.4	11.2	10.8
Phase, Deg.			

Analysis

1. Use the node voltage method to calculate the voltages at nodes nA, nB, and nC for the balanced circuit. Save the equation on your calculator for the next step.

2. Use the node voltage method to calculate the voltages at nodes nA, nB, and nC for the unbalanced load circuit (edit your equation from step 1). Refer to the TI-89 example on the next page.

3. Calculate the percent difference between the measured and calculated values of the voltages at nodes nA, nB, and nC for the balanced and unbalanced loads.

115

4. Calculate the voltage across each load resistor using the measured results for the voltages at nA, nB, and nC. [$(V_{nA} - V_{nB})$, $(V_{nB} - V_{nC})$, and $(V_{nC} - V_{nA})$]

PSpice Example

Results for the circuit on the right.

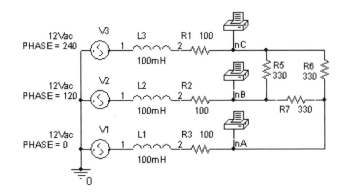

FREQ	VM(NC)	VP(NC)
60	6.187	-130.2

FREQ	VM(NB)	VP(NB)
60	6.187	109.8

FREQ	VM(NA)	VP(NA)
60	6.187	-10.18

TI-89 Example

Let $V(nA) = x$, $V(nB) = y$, $V(nC) = z$.

Equations:

$$\frac{x-12\angle0}{100+37.7i}+\frac{x-y}{330}+\frac{x-z}{330}=0 \text{ and } \frac{y-12\angle120}{100+37.7i}+\frac{y-x}{330}+\frac{y-z}{330}=0 \text{ and } \frac{z-12\angle240}{100+37.7i}+\frac{z-x}{330}+\frac{z-y}{330}=0$$

TI-89 input:

Balanced case:

csolve((x-12)/(100+37.7i)+(x-y)/330+(x-z)/330=0 and (y-(12∠120))/(100+37.7i)+(y-x)/330+(y-z)/330=0 and (z-(12∠240))/(100+37.7i)+(z-x)/330+(z-y)/330=0,{x,y,z})

x = (6.187∠-10.8)   y = (6.187∠109.8)   z = (6.187∠-130.2)

Unbalanced case:

csolve((x-12)/(100+37.7i)+(x-y)/330+(x-z)/220=0 and (y-(12∠120))/(100+37.7i)+(y-x)/330+(y-z)/330=0 and (z-(12∠240))/(100+37.7i)+(z-x)/220+(z-y)/330=0,{x,y,z})

x = (5.611∠-15.12)   y = (6.187∠109.82)   z = (5.477∠-127.29)

116

Experiment 31: Series RLC Circuit Step Response

Introduction

A step response is generated when the input to a circuit changes instantaneously from one value to another value. A function generator will be used as a step source by setting it to produce a 5 V peak-to-peak square wave with an offset of 2.5 V. The period of the square wave is set so that the circuit returns to steady state before the next step occurs.

The circuit will exhibit a "forced" step response when the generator voltage transitions from 0 to 5 V. During this time energy is being forced into the circuit. The circuit will reach steady state when the capacitor charges to 5 V and the circuit current goes to zero. When the generator voltage transitions from 5 V to 0 V the circuit will exhibit a "natural" response. During this time the circuit's stored energy is dissipated.

Forced Step Response

The step response of a circuit is observed when the voltage applied to it changes instantly from one value to another.

A 5 V DC source is applied to the circuit on the right. When the switch closes at t = 0 the forced step response is observed as Vo across the 220 Ω resistor.

An s-domain version is shown on the right.

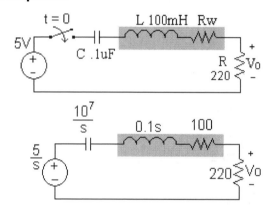

$$\frac{Vo}{Vs}=\frac{R}{R+Rw+Ls+\dfrac{1}{Cs}}=\frac{\left(\dfrac{R}{L}\right)s}{s^2+\left(\dfrac{R+Rw}{L}\right)s+\dfrac{1}{LC}}=\frac{2200\,s}{s^2+\left(3200\right)s+1\times10^8}$$

$$Vo=\frac{2200\,s}{s^2+\left(3200\right)s+1\times10^8}\left(\frac{5}{s}\right)=\frac{11000}{(s+1600-j9871)(s+1600+j9871)}$$

.

The time domain result is: $v_0(t)=1.114e^{-1600t}\sin(9871t)$

This circuit exhibits an under-damped forced step response. Its damped frequency is 9871 radians per second and decay rate is 1600 nepers per second.

Natural Response

The natural response of a circuit is observed when a circuit dissipates its stored energy. For example, a capacitor charged to 5 V is discharged at t = 0. The resulting response is observed as the voltage Vo across the 220 Ω resistor.

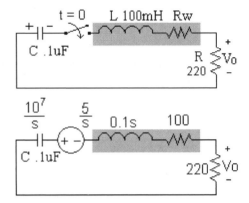

Time domain and s-domain versions of the circuit are shown on the right. Solving for Vo in the s-domain results in:

$$Vo = \frac{2200s}{s^2 + (3200)s + 1 \times 10^8} \left(\frac{-5}{s} \right) = \frac{-11000}{(s + 1600 - j9871)(s + 1600 + j9871)}$$

.

The time domain result is: $v_0(t) = -1.114e^{-1600t} \sin(9871t)$

This circuit exhibits an under-damped natural step response. Its damped frequency is 9871 radians per second and decay rate is 1600 nepers per second. The response is identical to the forced step response except for the negative sign.

This is the result obtained if a 5 V square wave with a 2.5 V offset were applied to the circuit with a long enough period so that the circuit returns to steady state during each half cycle.

The forced and natural responses are identical except that the natural response is 180 degrees out of phase with the forced response (negative sign).

Objectives

This lab exercise will demonstrate the production, measurement, and evaluation of the step response of a series RLC circuit.

Procedure

※ Inductor was bad

Equipment and Parts

Function Generator, Oscilloscope, Breadboard.
L = 100 mH, C = .1 uF capacitor, R = 220 Ω, R = 2200 Ω.

1.	Measure and record the resistance of the resistor, R, and inductor, Rw. If possible, measure the inductance of the inductor and capacitance of the capacitor.

R$_{220}$ _216_   R$_{2200}$ _2.168_   Rw _70.81_

L _100.1_   C _0.106_

Connect C, L, and R directly together, with no wires in between.

Connect the function generator and oscilloscope leads directly to the parts.

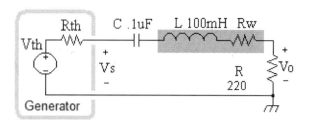

2. Set the function generator to produce a 100 Hz, 5 V peak-to-peak square wave, with a 2.5 V offset, when it is <u>not connected</u> to the circuit.

3. Use R equal to 220 Ω. Connect the function generator to the circuit. Channel 1 of the scope monitors the circuit's input, Vs, and channel 2 monitors output, Vo.

4. Set the time base to 1 mS per division. Trigger on channel 1, positive slope. The display should be similar to that on the right.

5. Set channel 1 to 2 V/DIV and channel 2 to 500 mV/DIV.

    Observe the relationship of the square wave to the damped sinusoidal waveform. Set the oscilloscope to DC input coupling and center both channels. Also note the oscillation on the channel 1 waveform.

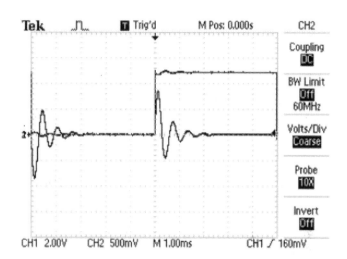

When the generator voltage changes from 0 to 5 V, a forced step response is observed. Note that the oscillation begins on the positive half cycle and decays exponentially. When the generator voltage changes from 5 V to 0 V, a natural response is observed.

Note the similarities and differences between the natural and the forced response (compare the amplitude and phase of the forced response and the natural response).

6. Change the oscilloscope's time base to 200 or 250 µS/DIV. With the trigger on channel 1, negative slope, display only channel 2. The entire natural response should be observed. You can further expand the waveform to measure the period more accurately

7. Determine and record the period of the damped oscillation, T_d, by measuring the time between zero crossings of the same slope.

    T_d ___2.41 mS___

119

Record the magnitude and time of occurrence of the first two positive peaks. Solve the exponential equations simultaneously (equations for v1 and v2 are given below) for the peak value, Vp, and decay rate, α. Organize your data into a table such as the one below:

Positive Peaks	220 ohm resistor	
	Time	Voltage
1st peak	488 ns	740 mV
2nd peak	1.14 ms	200 mV

$$v1=(Vp)e^{-\alpha(t1)}, \qquad v2=(Vp)e^{-\alpha(t2)}$$

8. Repeat the procedure using a 2200 Ω resistor for R. Set up the oscilloscope to get a display of both the forced and natural response (response should be over-damped).

9. Adjust the oscilloscope to observe the natural response and expand the display to measure and record the following as accurately as possible:

a) Amplitude and time of occurrence of the negative peak, T_P.

b) Time when the amplitude decays to 20% of its the maximum value $T_{20\%}$.

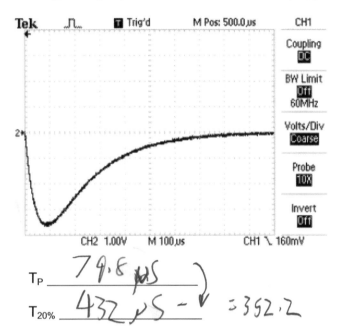

V_P -6.6√   ⟶ 3.3√

$V_{20\%}$ -1.32

T_P 79.8 µs

$T_{20\%}$ 432 µS - ✓ = 352.2

Analysis

1. Calculate the theoretical response of the circuit using your measured part values for R equal to 220 Ω and for R equal to 2200 Ω.

   Explain why the internal resistance of the function generator must be included in the calculations.

2. Compare the natural response results of the experiment with the 220 Ω resistor to theoretical calculations.

   Indicate response type. Compare the decay rate, α, and damped oscillation frequency, ω_d, by calculating the percent difference between the measurements and the theoretical calculations.

120

3. Compare the natural response results of the experiment with the 2200 Ω resistor to theoretical calculations.

   Compare the peak voltage V_P and time of occurrence, T_P by calculating the percent difference between the measurements and the theoretical calculations.

   Compare the theoretical time of occurrence $T_{20\%}$, of the 20% amplitude, $V_{20\%}$, by calculating the percent difference between the measurements and the theoretical calculations.

4. Optional: Simulate the circuit and compare simulated results to measured results. See example simulations below.

PSpice Example: RLC Step Response

"Vpulse" was used as the source for a 100Hz square wave with the settings shown in the circuit diagram on the right.

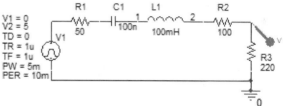

A transient simulation was run for 10mS to generate the graph on the right.

Cursors can be used to measure the peak voltages and their time of occurrence.

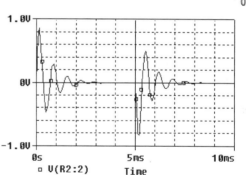

LTspice Example: RLC Step Response

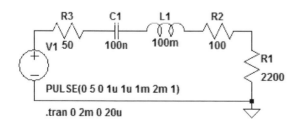

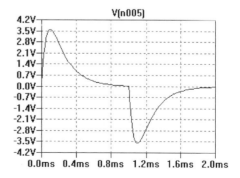

121

Experiment 32: RLC Circuit Impulse Response

Introduction

The unit impulse function, $\delta(t)$, has the properties of infinite amplitude, unit area, and infinitely short duration. This function is useful in the mathematical analysis of systems where the duration of the input excitation is much shorter than the system's response time.

A unit impulse can be scaled by the area of the excitation. This is the strength of the impulse. A rectangular voltage pulse with amplitude of 5 V and time duration of 3 microseconds has an area of 15-volt-microseconds. Its impulse function strength is 15-volt-microseconds.

A short duration exponential voltage, such as shown on the right, can be generated by applying a square wave to an RC circuit. This exponential voltage can be represented by an impulse function whose strength is equal to the area of the exponential voltage. The area can be calculated:

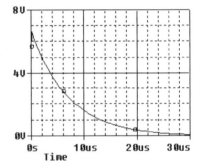

$$A = V_P \int_0^\infty e^{-\alpha t} dt = 6.5 \int_0^\infty e^{-143000t} dt = 45.5\,\mu V - \sec.$$

V_P is the peak amplitude at t equal to zero. The decay rate, α, is the reciprocal of its time constant. Its impulse function can be expressed as: $45.5\delta(t)$.

If this impulse function is applied to an RLC circuit whose response time is much longer than the duration of the impulse, the result of the calculation will closely approximate the actual response of the circuit.

Given that Vs in the RLC circuit on the right can be represented by an impulse function, $A\delta(t)$, the circuit's response in the s-domain is calculated as:

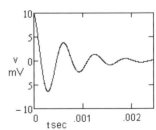

$Vs = (3.125 \times 10^{-6})\delta(t)$

$$H(s) = \frac{\dfrac{R}{L}s}{s^2 + \dfrac{R}{L}s + \dfrac{1}{LC}} = \frac{3200s}{s^2 + 3200s + 10^8}, \qquad Vo(s) = A \cdot H(S).$$

Vo(s) is the RLC circuit's s-domain impulse response, where "A" is the strength of the impulse. In this case, "A" is the area under the voltage versus time curve of the exponential source, Vs.

Solution:

$$v = e^{-1600t}[10\cos(9871t) - 1.62\sin(9871t)]\,mV$$

Note that the circuit's impulse response is similar to its step response.

Objectives

A circuit's impulse response may be calculated mathematically using the Dirac delta function as the input "forcing function". This lab experiment uses an exponential voltage source whose time constant is much shorter than the response time of the circuit. This source is applied to an under-damped series RLC circuit.

The response of the circuit will be compared to mathematical analysis using a Dirac delta function whose strength is approximated as the area under the exponential voltage versus time curve.

Procedure

Equipment and Parts

Function Generator, Oscilloscope, Breadboard.
L = 100 mH, C1 = 47 nF, C2 = 100 nF, R1 = 100 Ω, R2 = 390 Ω.
Rth = Function generator resistance, Rw = Inductor DC resistance.

1. Measure the value of the resistors, R1 and R2, and inductor resistance, Rw.

    R1 _____   R2 _____   C1 _____

    C2 _____   L _____   Rw _____

2. Connect the function generator to the oscilloscope channel 1 but don't connect it to the circuit yet. Set the function generator to produce a 200 Hz square wave, offset so the waveform goes from 0 to 10 V (no load).

3. Connect the circuit on the right. The source, Vs, and Rth represent the function generator.

4. Connect channel 1 across R1 to measure Vi. Expand the display for best accuracy.

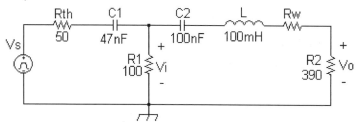

Vi's amplitude decays to 0.37 of its maximum value in one time constant. The graph of Vi on the right shows a maximum amplitude of 7 V and time constant of 6.5 microseconds

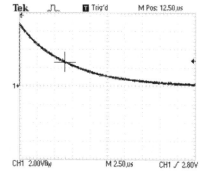

The decay rate, α, is the reciprocal of the time constant. In this case, α is 153,800 nepers per second. The time domain equation for this response is:

$$Vi(t) = 7e^{-133800t}.$$

123

The strength of the impulse can now be calculated as the area under the exponential curve:

$$A = 7\int_0^\infty e^{-153800t} dt = 45.5\mu V - sec.$$

Record your results: Vi(max) _____   α _____

5.   Connect channel 2 to measure Vo. Set the timing to 500 μS/DIV, channel 1 to 5 V/DIV and channel 2 to 200 mV/DIV. Trigger on channel 1and positive slope.

6.   Set the oscilloscope to 100 μS/DIV. Adjust the oscilloscope to obtain the display on the right.

Note the pulse on channel 1 and its timing relationship to the RLC response on channel 2.

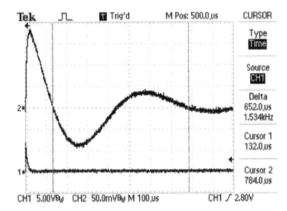

7.   Measure and record the period, T, of the damped oscillation. The display above shows a period of 652 μS. Do not use the first half cycle.

        T _____

8.   Adjust the oscilloscope so that you can measure the amplitudes and times of occurrence of the positive and negative peaks. If possible, acquire the data directly from the oscilloscope to a spreadsheet file for later analysis.

Measure and record as accurately as possible the absolute values of the magnitudes of the positive and negative peaks and times of their occurrence (ignore the first peak near t = 0).

V_{P1} _____ t_1 _____ V_{P2} _____ t_2 _____

Analysis

1.   Use the data from procedure step 4 to calculate the strength of the impulse applied to the RLC circuit.

2.   Use the result of procedure step 7 to calculate the damped oscillation frequency. Use the result of procedure step 8 to calculate the decay rate.

Solve simultaneously for V_P and α: $V_{P1} = V_p e^{-\alpha t_1}$ $V_{P2} = V_p e^{-\alpha t_2}$

3.   Use a math program, such as *MATLAB* or *Maple*, to calculate the impulse response of the series RLC circuit using the strength of the impulse calculated in analysis step 1 above. Use your measured part values.

124

4. Compare the parameters of your calculated response to your experimental results. Indicate the differences in the amplitude, decay rate, and damped oscillation frequency, in percent.

5. Optional: Simulate the circuit using your part values. See example PSpice simulation below. The first circuit uses the exponential pulse generated by the RC circuit. The second circuit uses a rectangular pulse of approximately the same area. They both produce approximately the same response.

PSpice Simulation

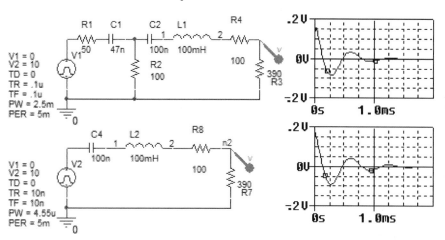

LTspice Simulation:

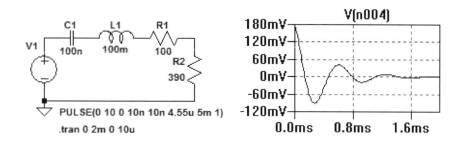

Experiment 33: Inductive Surge Voltage

Introduction

An instantaneous change in an inductor's current can produce surge voltage which may damage electronic components. Surge suppressors are often used to reduce this effect.

Consider the circuit on the right. When the switch is opened, the current through the inductor must change from 10mA to 5.45 mA. Since the inductor has an inertia to a change in current, the voltage across it instantaneously increases to maintain the higher current of 10 mA. The current then decays exponentially to a steady state value of 5.45 mA.

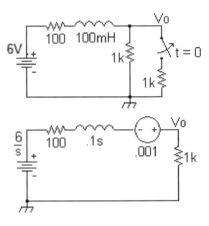

The switching operation is modeled in the s-domain for t > 0 on the right. The current before the switch is opened is the initial condition for the inductor for t < 0. Refer to the s-domain equation for Vo and the time domain solution, Vo(t), below.

$$Vo(s) = \frac{1000\left(\dfrac{6}{s} + .001\right)}{.1s + 1100}$$

$$Vo(t) = 5.45 + 4.55\,e^{-11000t}$$

Vo(t) is 10 V at t = 0. I decays exponentially to 5.45 V. Vo surges to a voltage that is 4 V higher than the battery voltage.

Objectives

This experiment will demonstrate the creation of an inductive surge voltage caused by a change in load current. A transistor switch will repetitively connect and disconnect a load resistance. A square wave voltage from the function generator turns the transistor switch on and off at a frequency of 500 Hz. The resulting output voltage is observed on an oscilloscope. The results will be compared to theoretical calculations.

Procedure

Equipment and Parts

Power supply, Function Generator, Oscilloscope with X10 probes, Breadboard.
L = 100 mH, R1a = 1200 Ω, R1b = 3300 Ω, R2 = 820 Ω.
R3 = 4700 Ω. Transistor = 2N3904 or equivalent.

---

1.   Measure the values of the resistors, R1a, R1b, R2, and inductor resistance, Rw. If possible, measure the inductance of the inductor, L.

   R1a _____   R1b _____   R2 _____   Rw _____   L _____

126

2. Connect the circuit on the right. Set the function generator to produce a 500 Hz, 5 V peak-to-peak square wave with a plus 2.5 V offset. R1 = R1a.

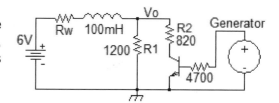

3. Connect channel 1 of the oscilloscope to the function generator and channel 2 to measure Vo. Trigger on channel 1.

4. Adjust the oscilloscope's time per division and volts per division to observe about one cycle of the Vo waveform on channel 2.

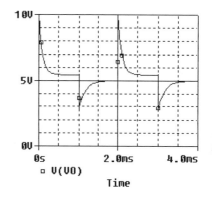

The plot on the right was produced with R1 and R2 equal to 1000 Ω.   When the transistor switch turns off, a positive exponential pulse is generated which decays to a steady state value of 5.4 V.   When the transistor switch turns on, a negative pulse is generated which decays to a steady state value of 5 V.

5. Measure and record the peak amplitude of the positive pulse, V_{P+} (V_{P+} is equal to the pulse's maximum positive value minus its steady state value).   The graph above shows a maximum positive value of 9.6 V and a steady value of 5.4 V so that its V_{P+} value is 4.2 V. Its amplitude decays to 6.95 V in one time constant, and τ_+ is about 0.1 seconds.   Expand the display to make accurate measurements.

V_{P+} _____ τ_+ _____ V_{SS+} _____

6. Measure and record the peak amplitude of the negative pulse, $V_{P-,}$ its decay time constant, τ_- , and steady state voltage, V_{SS-}.

V_{P-} _____ τ_- _____ V_{SS} _____

7. Turn off power supply and Replace R1a with R1b.   Turn on power supply.

8. Measure and record the peak amplitude of the positive pulse, V_{P+},   its decay time constant, τ_+ , and steady state voltage, V_{SS+}.

V_{P+} _____ τ_+ _____ V_{SS+} _____

9. Measure and record the peak amplitude of the negative pulse, $V_{P-,}$ its decay time constant, τ_- , and steady state voltage, V_{SS-}.

V_{P-} _____ τ_- _____ V_{SS-} _____

127

Analysis

1. Calculate the theoretical response of the circuit with R1a and R1b. Compare your calculations to your measurements. Express the percent differences between the theoretical and measured results for the peak amplitude, time constant, and steady state voltage for both the positive and negative exponential pulses.

    Note that the transistor is not a perfect switch. It has a small "on" resistance, typically less than 100 Ω, and an "off" resistance which is typically above 100,000 Ω.

2. Simulate the circuit and compare the simulated results to your calculated results.

    Refer to the example simulation below. Be sure to use your measured part values in your simulation.

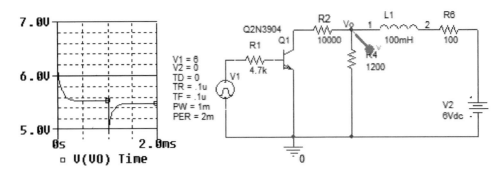

Maple Example: Inductive Surge Voltage

R1 = R2 = 1000-ohms.

```
>  with(inttrans);
```

```
> Vo:=((1000)*((6/s)+(.001)))/(.1*s+1100);
```

$$Vo := \frac{1000\left(\dfrac{6}{s} + 0.001\right)}{0.1\,s + 1100}$$

```
> vx:=invlaplace(Vo,s,t);
```

$$vx := 5.454545455 + 4.545454545 e^{-11000.\,t}$$

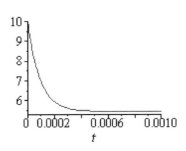

```
> plot(vx,t=0..1e-3);
```

128

Experiment 34: Inductive Impulse Voltage

Introduction

Switching operations in inductive circuits can produce voltage impulses, short duration and possibly high amplitude voltage spikes. Consider the circuit below. Before the switch opens the circuit current is 1.2 mA, limited by R1. The instant the switch opens the current drops to 0.6 mA, limited by R1 plus R2. The rapid change in current creates a voltage impulse across L1, as shown in the graphs below.

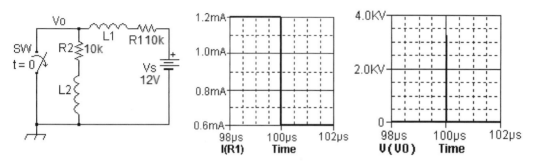

The magnitude of the voltage is over 3000 V and the duration is very short. This is because inductors oppose a change of current. L2 acts like an open circuit initially, so that L1 is discharging into a very high resistance, which means a very short discharge time constant and large voltage amplitude. This impulse may be modeled by the Dirac delta function.

A load resistance, R3, is connected across the switch in the circuit below. The discharge time constant is increased and the magnitude of the peak voltage is decreased to about 55 volts. The magnitude of the exponential voltage spike increases as the value of R3 is increased. Some of the energy stored in L1 is discharged into R3. Note the circuit and graphs below.

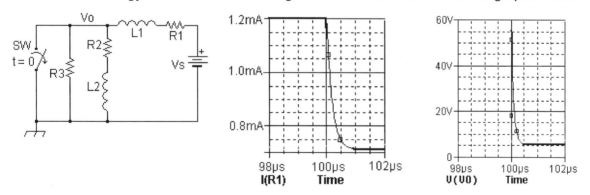

Objectives

This experiment uses a transistor as an electronic switch. Its breakdown voltage is 40 V, so the amplitude of the voltage spike must be less than that. The impulse response for two different values of load resistors will be measured and analyzed. One objective is to show that the duration of the exponential spike decreases, and the voltage magnitude increases, as the value of the load resistor increases.

Procedure

Equipment and Parts

Power supply, Function Generator. Oscilloscope with X10 probes, Breadboard.
L1 = 100 mH,   L2 = 100 mH.   Transistor = 2N3904 or equivalent.
Resistors: 2.2 KΩ, three 1 KΩ, all ¼ watt, 5%.

---

1.   Measure and record the resistance of the inductors, Rw1 and Rw2.

   Rw1: _____   Rw2: _____

   Resistor and inductor values don't need to be measured (except for the resistance of the inductors). Their labeled values will be used in the analysis.   The objective of this experiment is to show that an impulsive response is produced by the inductive load.

2.   Connect the circuit in Figure A below. Set the function generator to produce a 5 V peak-to-peak, 1 KHz square wave, with a plus 2.5 V offset.

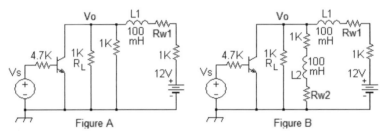

Figure A   Figure B

3.   Connect channel 1 of the oscilloscope to the function generator and channel 2 to measure Vo.   Trigger on channel 1.

4.   Adjust the oscilloscope's time per division and volts per division to observe about one cycle of the Vo waveform on channel 2.

5.   Measure and record the peak amplitude of the positive pulse, V_P, (about 1.8 V in the graph on the right), the time constant, τ, and the steady state voltage, V_{SS} (4.9 V in the graph on the right). This is a surge voltage similar to that in experiment 33.

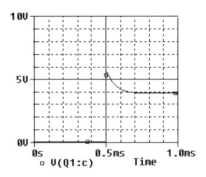

   V_P _____ τ _____ V_{SS} _____

6.   Connect the circuit in Figure B above (add the inductor L2 to the load circuit). Set the function generator to produce a 5 V peak-to-peak, 1 KHz square wave, with a plus 2.5 V offset.

130

7. Connect channel 1 of the oscilloscope to the function generator and channel 2 to measure Vo. Trigger on channel 1. Adjust the oscilloscope's time per division and volts per division to observe about one cycle of the Vo waveform on channel 2, as shown on the right.

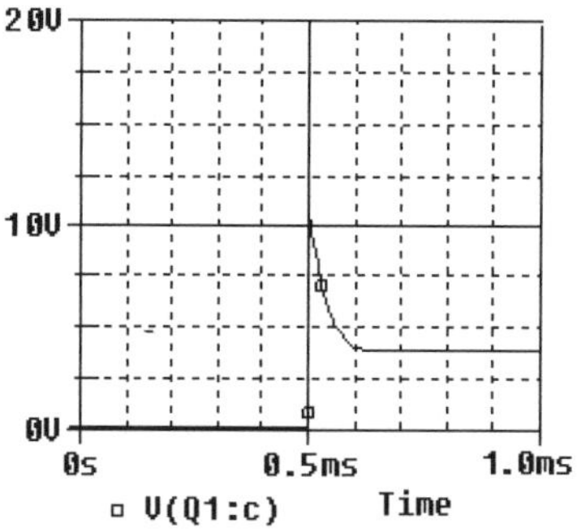

U(Q1:c)   Time

8. Expand the oscilloscope display by adjusting the volts per division, time per division, and trigger controls to most accurately measure the peak amplitude of the positive pulse, V_P, its decay time constant, τ, and steady state voltage, V_{SS}.

    V_P _____ τ _____ V_{SS} _____

9. Turn off power supply and change the value of R_L to 2.2 KΩ. Turn on the power supply. Expand the oscilloscope display by adjusting the volts per division, time per division, and trigger controls to accurately measure the peak amplitude of the positive pulse, V_P, its decay time constant, τ, and steady state voltage, V_{SS}. Record below.

    V_P _____ τ _____ V_{SS} _____

10. Turn off power supply and change the value of R_L to 3.3K. Turn on the power supply. Expand the oscilloscope display by adjusting the volts per division, time per division, and trigger controls to accurately measure and record the peak amplitude of the positive pulse, V_P, its decay time constant, τ, and steady state voltage, V_{SS}.

    V_P _____ τ _____ V_{SS} _____

Analysis

1. Calculate the theoretical response of the circuit in Figure A and compare the results to your measurements in procedure step 5.

2. Calculate the theoretical response of the circuit in Figure B with R_L equal to 1 KΩ. Compare results to your measurements in procedure step 8.

3. Simulate the circuit in Figure B with R_L equal to 2.2 KΩ and 3.3 KΩ or use a math program such as *Maple* or *MATLAB*.

    Compare your results to the measurements in steps 9 and 10. Explain how the results show that the response approaches an impulse as the value of R_L increases.

131

Maple Example: Inductive Impulse Voltage

Response for $R_L = \infty$.

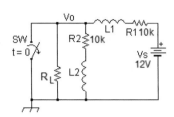

```
> restart;
> with(inttrans);
> I1:=(12/s+0.12e-3)/(20000+.2*s);
> V1:=I1*(10000+.1*s);
> V1t:=invlaplace(V1,s,t);
```
$$V1t := 0.00006000000000 \mathrm{Dirac}(t) + 6.$$

Response for R_L = 30K.

```
> I2:=(12/s+0.12e-3)/(10000+.1*s+(30000*(.1*s+30000))/(60000+.1*s));
> V2:=I2*(30000*(.1*s+30000))/(60000+.1*s);
> V2t:=invlaplace(V2, s, t);
```
$$V2t := 7.200000000$$
$$+ 7.200000000 e^{-5.00000\ 10^5\ t} \left(4.\cosh(3.16227766010^5\ t) \right.$$
$$\left. - 3.162277660 \sinh(3.16227766010^5\ t) \right)$$

```
> plot(V2t, t = 0 .. 0.1e-4);
```

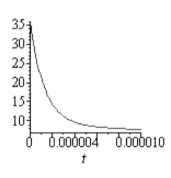

The area under the pulse is calculated below. It can be shown that as the value of R_L approaches infinity, the area approaches the strength of the impulse of .00006 volt-seconds.

```
> int(V2t-7.2,t=0..infinity);
```
$$0.0000480000000$$

Experiment 35: Low-Pass Filters and Integrators

Low Pass Filters

Low pass filters are used to pass frequencies below a parameter called the "cutoff frequency", and to reject frequencies above the cutoff frequency. The cutoff frequency is defined as the frequency where the power output of the filter is one half of the power input. This occurs when the magnitude of the output voltage is equal to the magnitude of the input voltage divided by the square root of two.

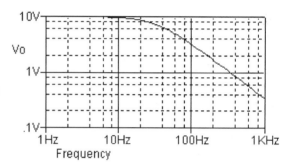

Figure A

The magnitude of the transfer function and the cutoff frequency of the circuit in Figure A on the right are given by:

$$\frac{V_o}{V_{in}} = \frac{1}{\sqrt{1 + (2\pi f RC)^2}} \qquad f_c = \frac{1}{2\pi RC} = 33.865\,\text{Hz.}$$

A log-log plot of the frequency response of the low-pass filter is shown on the right. Vo is 7.07 volts (-3 dB) at the cutoff frequency of 34 hertz. Vo decreases by a factor of 10 for each decade increase of frequency beyond the cutoff frequency (-20 dB/decade).

Integrators

A simple RC circuit, such as the one in Figure A above, may also be used as an integrator. The output voltage of an ideal integrator circuit is directly proportional to time if a constant input voltage is applied.

$$v_o(t) = k\int_0^t v_{in}(\tau)d\tau = k\,v_{in}t \quad \text{if } v_{in} \text{ is a constant.}$$

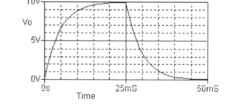

The graph above on the right shows the response of an RC circuit, such as the one in Figure A, to a square wave. The response is approximately linear for the first few milliseconds of the charging half cycle and the first few milliseconds of the discharging half cycle. This is about 10% of the circuit's time constant.

Increasing the frequency of the square wave applied to the circuit in Figure A shortens the charge and discharge time of the capacitor.

The graphs of Vo below show that the output approaches a triangle wave as the frequency is increased to 200 Hz. This shows that a low pass filter makes a pretty good integrator for input frequencies more than one decade above the cutoff frequency.

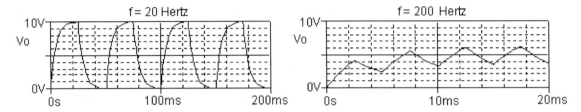

The first circuit shown below is an "ideal op-amp integrator". But it is not practical because the circuit develops an unpredictable offset voltage.

The second circuit is an op-amp implementation of the simple RC integrator. It has the advantage that its input impedance is constant and its output impedance is essentially zero. The s-domain transfer functions are given for all three integrators.

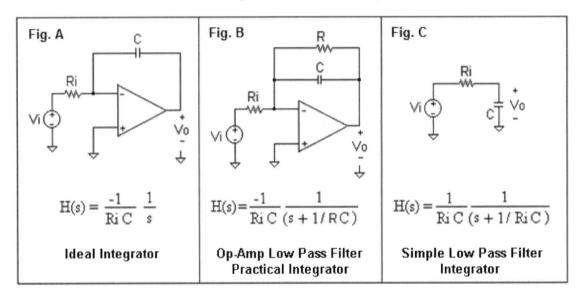

Note the transfer functions for each of the circuits above.

Figure A is an ideal integrator because dividing by s in the s-domain is the same as integrating in the time domain.

Figure B approaches an ideal integrator as the term 1/RC approaches zero (as R increases, the filter's cutoff frequency decreases).

Both figures B and C are good integrators only for frequencies that are at least one decade above the filter's cutoff frequency.

Objectives

In part 1 of this experiment the frequency response of a low pass filter will be plotted and compared to theoretical calculations. In part two the low pass filter will be evaluated as an integrator.

Procedure

Equipment and Parts

Function Generator, Oscilloscope with X10 probes, Breadboard.
$L1 = 100$ mH, $L2 = 100$ mH. Transistor = 2N3904 or equivalent.

Part 1: Low-Pass Filter

1. Measure the value of the resistor, and if possible, the capacitor.

    Ri _____   C _____

2. Connect the circuit on the right. Connect oscilloscope channel 1 to the function generator, Vi, and channel 2 to measure Vo.

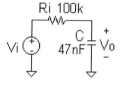

3. Set the trigger to channel 1 and positive slope. Set the oscilloscope to measure the amplitude and phase of Vo with respect to Vi. Set the function generator to produce a 10 Hz, 10-volt peak-to-peak, sine wave.

4. Measure the amplitude and phase angle of Vo at 10, 20, 100, 1000, and 10,000Hz. Record the data in the table below.

    Measure the frequency and phase angle of Vo at the frequencies where the amplitude of Vo is 8.50, 7.07, and 5.00 V peak-to-peak. Record the data in the table below.

Frequency Hz	Vo volts p-p	Θ Degrees
10		
20		
	8.50	
	7.07	
	5.00	
100		
1000		
10,000		

Part 2: Integrator

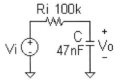

1. Connect the circuit on the right.

2. Connect oscilloscope channel 1 to the function generator, Vi, and channel 2 to measure Vo. Also connect the DMM to measure the DC value of Vo.

3. Set the trigger to channel 1 and positive slope.

4. Set the generator to produce a 20 Hz, 10 V peak-to-peak, square wave with a 5 V offset so it goes from 0 to 10 V. Measure and record Vo p-p and sketch or capture one cycle of the output waveform.

   Vo _____ volts p-p

5. Repeat step 4 at 200 Hz.   Vo _____ volts p-p

6. Repeat step 4 at 2000 Hz.   Vo _____ volts p-p

   Label and scale the vertical and horizontal axis of your sketches or captures.

Analysis, Part 1

1. Plot the frequency response of the filter on semi-log paper. Plot the frequency on the log axis and amplitude in dB on the vertical axis ($dB = 20 \log Vo$).

2. Calculate the filter's cutoff frequency and the percent difference between the measured and calculated value.

3. Calculate the filter's attenuation in dB per decade using the amplitudes at 1000 Hz and 10,000 Hz. Compare result to theoretical value.

Analysis, Part 2

1. Explain the results of procedure part 2, steps 4, 5, and 6, in terms of peak-to-peak amplitude and linearity of Vo, and the quality of the integration.

2. Solve for the response of the circuit in Figure A to a step voltage input. Solve in the s-domain and transform the result to the time domain. Use your solution to explain the results of procedure part 2, steps 4, 5, and 6.

3. Optional: Simulate the circuit using PSpice or LTspice. Compare the simulated results to your measured and calculated results.

4. Optional: Use a series expansion of the exponential function about t = 0 to compare "non-ideal" integrators to ideal integrators. How is the result related to frequency? Refer to the Taylor series in the appendix.

Experiment 36: High-Pass Filters and Differentiators

High-Pass Filters

High-pass filters are used to pass frequencies above a parameter called the "cutoff frequency", and to reject frequencies below the cutoff frequency. The cutoff frequency is defined as the frequency where the power output of the filter is half of the power input. This occurs when the magnitude of the output voltage is equal to the magnitude of the input voltage divided by the square root of two.

The magnitude of the transfer function and the cutoff frequency of the circuit in figure A on the right are given by:

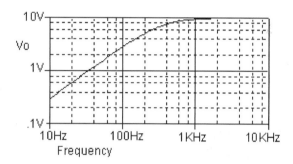

Figure A

$$\frac{V_o}{V_{in}} = \frac{1}{\sqrt{1 + (1/2\pi f RC)^2}} \qquad f_c = \frac{1}{2\pi RC} = 338.65 \, Hz.$$

A log-log plot of the frequency response of the high pass filter is shown on the right. Vo is 7.07 V (-3dB) at the cutoff frequency of 338 Hz. Vo decreases by a factor of 10 for each decade decrease of frequency below the cutoff frequency (-20dB/decade).

Differentiators

A simple RC circuit, such as the one in Figure A above may also be used as a differentiator. The output voltage of a differentiator is directly proportional to rate of change of the input voltage.

$$v_o(t) = k \frac{dv_{in}}{dt}$$

INPUT → **DIFFERENTIATOR** → **OUTPUT**

The voltage of a triangle wave increases and decreases linearly. An ideal differentiator converts a triangle wave to a square wave, as shown above.

This lab exercise will show that an RC high pass filter circuit is a good differentiator for frequencies that are more than an octave below its cutoff frequency.

The graph on the right shows the response of the circuit in Figure A to a 100 Hz triangle wave.

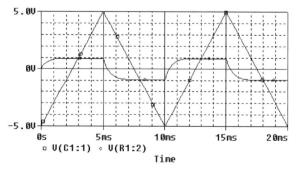

137

The output of an electronic voltage differentiator is ideally equal to the rate of change of its input voltage. Ideal differentiators, such as the circuit in Figure A below, are hard to implement. This is because the voltage gain of the circuit in Figure A is very high at high frequencies, causing the output to be noisy.

In Figure B, the resistor Ri is designed to limit the maximum gain of the op-amp. However, the circuit is not an ideal differentiator, but it can approximate one.

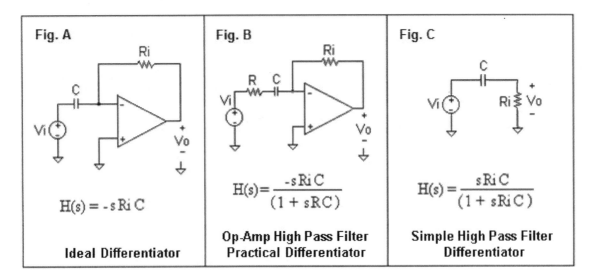

Fig. A

$$H(s) = -s\,Ri\,C$$

Ideal Differentiator

Fig. B

$$H(s) = \frac{-s\,Ri\,C}{(1 + sRC)}$$

Op-Amp High Pass Filter
Practical Differentiator

Fig. C

$$H(s) = \frac{s\,Ri\,C}{(1 + s\,Ri\,C)}$$

Simple High Pass Filter
Differentiator

Figure A is an ideal differentiator because multiplying by s in the s-domain is the same as differentiating in the time domain. However, the circuits in Figures B and C have a binomial in s term in their denominators.

Objectives

In part 1 of this experiment the frequency response of a high pass filter will be plotted and compared to theoretical calculations. In part two the high pass filter will be evaluated as an differentiator.

Procedure

Equipment and Parts

Function Generator, Oscilloscope with X10 probes, Breadboard.
R = 100 KΩ, ¼ watt, 5%. C = 47 nF, 5%.

Part1: High-Pass Filter

1.   Measure the value of the resistor, and if possible, the capacitor.

   R _____   C _____

2. Connect the circuit on the right. Connect channel 1 of the oscilloscope to the function generator, Vi, and channel 2 to measure Vo. Set the trigger to channel 1 and positive slope.

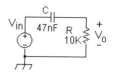

3. Set the oscilloscope to measure the amplitude of Vo and the phase angle of Vo with respect to Vi.

   Set the function generator to produce a 1000 Hz, 10 V peak-to-peak, sine wave.

4. Measure the amplitude and phase angle of Vo at 10, 100, 1000, and 10,000 Hz. Record the data in the table below.

   Measure the frequency and phase angle of Vo at the frequencies where the amplitude of Vo is 5.00, 7.07, and 8.50 V peak-to-peak. Record the data in the table below.

Frequency Hz	Vo volts p-p	Θ Degrees
10		
100		
	5.00	
	7.07	
	8.5	
1000		
10,000		

Part 2: Differentiator

1. Connect the circuit on the right.

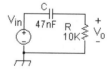

2. Connect channel 1 of the oscilloscope to the function generator, Vi, and channel 2 to measure Vo. Also connect the DMM to measure the DC value of Vo.

3. Set the trigger to channel 1 and positive slope.

4. Set the function generator to produce a 1000 Hz, 10 V peak-to-peak, triangle wave with no offset so it goes from -5 V to +5 V. Measure and record Vo p-p, and sketch or capture one cycle of the output waveform.

   Vo _____ volts p-p

5. Repeat step 4 at 100 Hz.   Vo _____ volts p-p

6. Repeat step 4 at 10 Hz.   Vo _____ volts p-p

   Label and scale the vertical and horizontal axis of your sketches or captures.

Analysis, Part 1

1. Plot the frequency response of the filter on semi-log paper. Plot the frequency on the log axis and amplitude in dB on the vertical axis ($dB = 20 \log Vo$).

2. Calculate the filter's cutoff frequency and the percent difference between the measured and calculated value.

3. Calculate the filter's attenuation in dB per decade using the amplitudes at 100 Hz and 10 Hz. Compare result to the theoretical value.

4. Optional: Simulate the frequency response of the filter with PSpice or LTspice.

Analysis, Part 2

1. Solve for the response of the circuit in Figure A to a ramp voltage input. Solve in the s-domain and transform result to the time domain. Use your solution to explain the results of procedure part 2, steps 4, 5, and 6.

2. Optional: Simulate the circuit using PSpice or LTspice. Compare the simulated results to your measured and calculated results.

Example PSpice Results

The simulation results below are at 1000 Hz (left) and at 100 Hz (right).

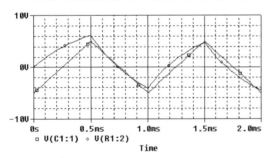
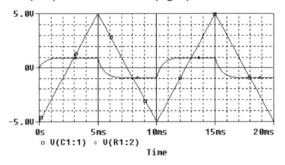

The triangle wave was generated using the part "VPWL_RE_FOREVER". To generate a 1000 Hz, 10 V peak-to-peak triangle wave, double click on the part to open its property editor.

Set the FIRST_NPAIRS, SECOND_NPAIRS, and THIRD_NPAIRS as shown below. To generate 100 Hz change the times to 5m and 10m. To generate 10 Hz change the times to 50m and 100m.

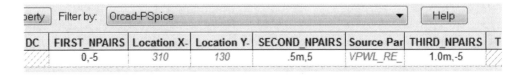

DC	FIRST_NPAIRS	Location X-	Location Y-	SECOND_NPAIRS	Source Par	THIRD_NPAIRS	T
	0,-5	310	130	.5m,5	VPWL_RE_	1.0m,-5	

Experiment 37: Band-Pass Filter Step Response / Convolution Integral

Introduction

A low-pass filter is cascaded with a high-pass filter to create a band-pass filter An op-amp buffer is used between the low-pass and high-pass filters. This filter is intended to pass the frequencies between the low-pass and high-pass filter's cutoff frequencies. This experiment will measure the time-domain step response of this filter.

It is possible to obtain the time-domain response of this circuit by solving the circuit in the s-domain and converting the result to the time-domain. It is sometimes necessary to solve for the time-domain response in the time-domain using the convolution integral method. This experiment is intended to show an application of the time-domain convolution method.

Objectives

A square wave, V1, will be applied to a two section band-pass filter. The first section is a high-pass filter consisting of C1 and R1. The second section is a low-pass filter consisting of C2 and R2. The time-domain unit step response will be measured for the high-pass filter as V2.

The waveform, V2, is applied to the low-pass filter through an op-amp "buffer". The buffer has a transfer function of "1" (output is exactly equal to the input). The buffer has very high input impedance so that it does not load down the high-pass filter, and very low output impedance so that it acts like an ideal source for the low-pass filter. This makes it possible to calculate the transfer function of each filter independently. The measurement results will be compared to calculations and *OrCAD PSpice* simulation.

Procedure

Equipment and Parts

Function Generator, Oscilloscope, DC Power Supply, Breadboard.
18 KΩ and 33 KΩ resistors. µA741 op-amp.
2 each, 0.1 µF polyester film capacitors.

---

1.   Measure the values of the parts.

       R1 _____   R2 _____   C1 _____   C2 _____

2.   Connect the circuit on the right. V1 is the generator set to produce a 20 Hz, 1 V peak-to-peak, square wave, with a plus 0.50 V offset.

3.   Connect oscilloscope channel 1 to V1 and channel 2 to V2.

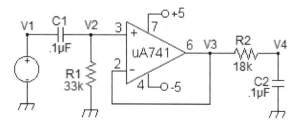

4. Set the oscilloscope's channels 1 and 2 to DC input coupling, and 0.5 V/DIV. Set the zero reference for channel 1 and 2 to the center of the screen.

5. Set the oscilloscope's time base to 5 mS per division, trigger to channel 1, positive slope. Observe channel 1 and carefully adjust the function generator's frequency and amplitude. You should observe exactly one cycle of the function generator waveform.

6. Observe channel 2 only (V2). You should see a waveform similar to the graph below on the left. Measure and record the time constant, τ, of the response by measuring as accurately as possible the time it takes for the waveform's amplitude to decay to exactly 0.368 V.

The reciprocal of the time constant is the decay rate, α, of the exponential response.

τ _____   α _____

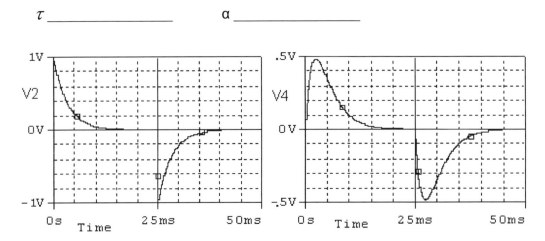

7. The signal V3 is the input to the low pass filter. Verify that the signal at the input of the low-pass filter is exactly the same as the signal V2 by moving the channel 2 scope probe to pin 6, V3, of the op-amp. Then move the channel 2 scope probe to display V4. You should observe a waveform similar to the graph above on the right.

8. Set the oscilloscope time base to 2 mS per division (or 2.5) and channel 2 vertical input to measure the signal amplitude as accurately as possible. Measure and record the amplitude, V_P, and the time of occurrence, t_P, of the positive peak.

V_P _____ t_P _____

If you are recording the measurements from the screen, try setting the zero reference to the bottom of the screen and set channel 1 volts per division for the largest display. Measure the amplitude of the positive amplitude response at 2 mS intervals.

If you are capturing data using a digital scope and capture software, set the vertical zero reference to exactly the center of the screen.

The objective is to record the response at the output of the low-pass filter as accurately as possible for comparison to theoretical expectation. Only the positive response will be analyzed.

142

Analysis

1. Simulate the band-pass filter circuit using transient analysis. Be sure to use the measured values of your components in the simulation.

2. Compare the following measured results with the simulated results:

    a) Amplitude and decay rate of the exponential waveform V2.

    b) Amplitude and time of occurrence of the positive peak of the response at V4.

    c) Express the percent error of the measurements of (a) and (b) above compared to the simulated results.

3. Use the convolution integral to calculate the response V2 to the input V1. Compare the results of your calculation to your measurements.

4. Use the convolution integral to calculate the response V4 to the input V3. Compare the results of your calculation to your measurements.

PSpice Example: Band-Pass Filter Pulse response

An ideal op amp, "OPAMP" from the analog library, is used in this simulation. It requires no power supply connections. The source "Vpulse" was set to produce a 20 millisecond pulse with a repetition rate of 40 milliseconds.

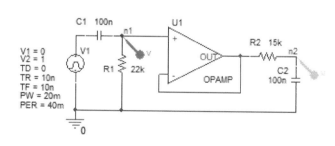 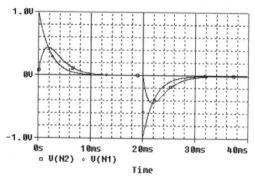

The pulse response of the high-pass filter section is observed at node n1 and the pulse response of the band-pass filter is observed at node n2.

Note that the 20 millisecond pulse width allows the high-pass filter section response and the low-pass filter section response to return to steady state in between each pulse.

LTspice Example: Band-Pass Filter Pulse response

This simulation uses the generic "opamp" in the opamp library. It is easy to use and requires no power supply connections. The directive, ".lib opamp.sub" must be added. Click on "op" on the right side of the main menu bar and type in the directive. It will be displayed on the schematic as shown below.

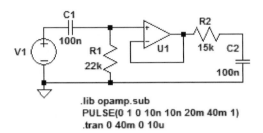

.lib opamp.sub
PULSE(0 1 0 10n 10n 20m 40m 1)
.tran 0 40m 0 10u

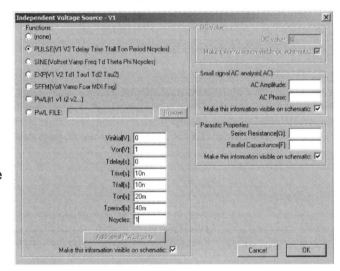

The source "Vpulse" was set to produce a 20 mS pulse with a repetition rate of 40 mS.

The band-pass filter's pulse response is plotted below. Note that the 20 millisecond pulse width allows the filter's response to return to steady state in between each pulse.

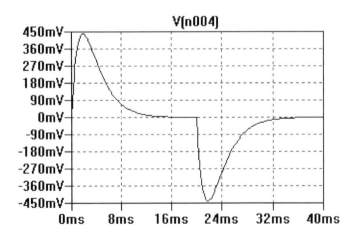

Experiment 38: Series Resonant Passive Band-Pass Filter

Introduction

The impedance of a series RLC circuit is a function of frequency. Since inductive reactance is directly proportional to frequency, and capacitive reactance is inversely proportional to frequency, there will be a frequency where they are equal. Since they have opposite signs their net reactance will be zero and the circuit's impedance will be purely resistive. Refer to the equations and circuit below.

$$X_L = 2\pi f L \qquad X_C = \frac{1}{2\pi f C} \qquad \mathbf{Z} = R + R_W + \mathbf{j}(X_L - X_C)$$

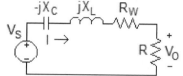

Series Resonance

The frequency where the reactances cancel is called the circuit's resonant frequency. In the circuit above, R_W is the resistance of the inductor. The circuit's transfer function, $\mathbf{T_s}$, is given below on the left. At the resonant frequency, the transfer function is $\mathbf{T_{s0}}$, below on the right.

$$\mathbf{T_s} = \frac{\mathbf{Vo}}{\mathbf{V_s}} = \frac{R}{(R_W + R) + \mathbf{j}(2\pi f L - \frac{1}{2\pi f C})} \qquad \mathbf{T_{so}} = \frac{R}{R_W + R} = 0.825.$$

The bandwidth, BW, of the circuit is defined as the difference between the upper and lower cutoff frequencies, f_2 and f_1. These two frequencies are defined as the frequencies where the value of the transfer function is equal to $1/\sqrt{2}$ of its value at resonance. These frequencies are also called the -3 dB frequencies because $1/\sqrt{2}$ is equal to -3 dB in units of decibels.

As a band-pass filter, this circuit will pass frequencies between f1 and f2 with an amplitude greater than $1/\sqrt{2}$ of the maximum value which occurs at the frequency, f_0.

Another important parameter of a resonant circuit is its quality factor, Q. It is defined as the ratio of the energy stored in the circuit to the energy dissipated by the circuit per cycle.

It can be shown that the circuit's bandwidth, BW, is related to Q and f_0 by the equations below:

$$Q = \frac{X_L}{R + R_W} = \frac{2\pi f_0 L}{R + R_W}, \qquad BW = \frac{f_0}{Q} = \frac{R + R_W}{2\pi L}.$$

Note that the bandwidth in units of radians per second is $(R + R_W)/L$. This is just the ratio of the circuit's resistance to its inductance.

If the circuit Q is large, larger than 5, the filter's cutoff frequencies will be symmetrical about the resonant frequency.

Objectives

In this experiment, the circuit's resonant frequency and bandwidth will be measured. The results will be compared to theory.

Procedure

Equipment and Parts

Function Generator, Oscilloscope with 10X probes, Breadboard.
Inductor: 100 mH, Capacitor: 1 nF, both 5%.
Resistors: R1 = 2200 Ω, R2 = 4700 Ω, both ¼ watt, 5%.

---

1. Measure and record the resistance of the resistors, R1 and R2, and inductor, Rw. If possible, measure the inductance of the inductor and capacitance of the capacitor

   R1 _____   R2 _____   Rw _____

   L _____   C _____

2. Connect the circuit on the right. Connect C, L, and R with no wires in between.

   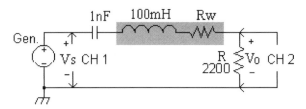

3. Set oscilloscope channel 1 to measure Vs. The function generator should have a 50 Ω or less output impedance.

   Set the function generator to produce a 16 KHz, 5 V, peak-to-peak sine wave, with no offset on channel 1 of the oscilloscope. Set the oscilloscope to trigger on channel 1. Set channel 2 to measure Vo.

4. Connect the function generator to the circuit. Fine-tune the generator to the frequency where Vo is maximum. Check that Vs = 5∠0° V p-p for steps 4 through 8.

5. Record the frequency and the magnitude of Vo. Measure and record the phase angle, θ_0, of Vo with respect to Vs.

   f_0 _____   Vo(max) _____ θ_0 _____

6. Adjust the function generator to a frequency below f_0 where Vo's magnitude is 0.707 of its maximum value. Record the frequency f_1. Measure and record the phase angle θ_1.

   f_1 _____   Vo(-3dB) _____ θ_1 _____

7. Adjust the function generator to a frequency above f_0 where Vo's magnitude is 0.707 (-3dB) of its maximum value. Record the frequency f_2. Measure and record angle θ_2.

   f_2 _____   Vo(-3dB) _____ θ_2 _____

8.   Replace the 2200 Ω resistor with the 4700 Ω. Repeat steps 3 through 7.
        Record your results below:

   f_0 _____   Vo(max) _____ θ_0 _____

   f_1 _____   Vo(-3dB) _____ θ_1 _____

   f_2 _____   Vo(-3dB) _____ θ_2 _____

Analysis

1.   Organize your data into a spreadsheet table such as the one below:

	A	B	C	D	E	F	G	H	I	J
1	Measured R = 2200 ohms					Simulated R = 2200 ohms				
3		Freq. Hz	Vo p-p	Vo Deg.			Freq. Hz	Vo p-p	Vo Deg.	% Error
4	Fo					Fo				
5	F1					F1				
6	F2					F2				
7	BW					BW				
9	Measured R = 4700 ohms					Simulated R = 4700 ohms				
11		Freq. Hz	Vo p-p	Vo Deg.			Freq. Hz	Vo p-p	Vo Deg.	% Error
12	Fo					Fo				
13	F1					F1				
14	F2					F2				
15	BW					BW				

        Use the measured values of your parts to do the calculations and simulations below.

2.   Transfer your measured results into the table. Calculate the theoretical values of the
        resonant frequencies and cutoff frequencies. Enter the results into the table.

3.   Enter equations into the appropriate cells to calculate BW and percent error.

4.   Simulate the circuit to check the results of your calculations. Refer to the simulation
        examples on the following pages.

5.   Optional exercise: Design a series resonant band-pass filter with a resonant frequency
        of 50 KHz and bandwidth of 10 KHz, using a 22 mH inductor with a winding resistance
        of 20 Ω.   Simulate the design and write a short report on the results.

147

PSpice Example: Series Resonant Band-Pass Filter

The circuit simulated here is identical to the circuit in the experiment. However, its part values, resonant frequency, and bandwidth are different. Use your measured part values.

"AC Sweep" analysis is used to plot the magnitude response of a series resonant RLC circuit from 100 Hz to 10,000 Hz. Use logarithmic sweep and 100 points per decade.

A circuit diagram and simulation results are shown below. Cursors are used to locate and measure the resonant frequency and maximum output (1.5849 KHz and 767.296 mV) and the upper cutoff frequency (1.9588 KHz).

The graph's horizontal axis could be expanded to improve the accuracy.

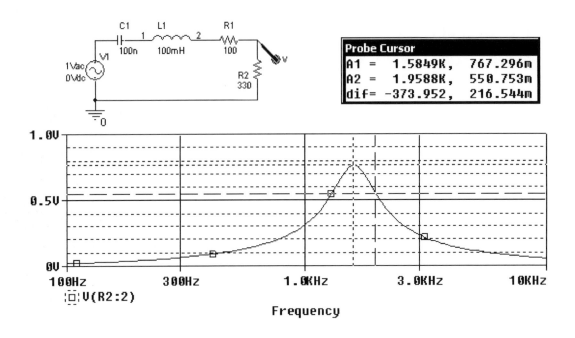

LTpice Example: Series Resonant Band-Pass Filter

This example uses a linear frequency sweep from 10K Hz to 25 KHz. V1 signal source magnitude is set to 5, and angle is set to 0.

The output voltage magnitude and phase are plotted on linear axis.

148

Right click on V1 to obtain the dialog box on the right.

The Function "SINE" is selected and the following settings are entered:

DC Offset = 0
Amplitude = 5
Freq. = 1k
AC Amplitude = 5
AC Phase = 0

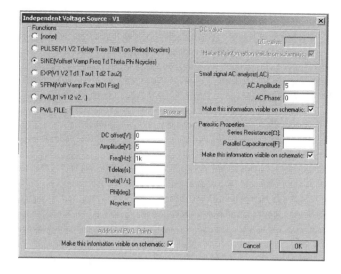

Click on Simulate in the main menu and select *Edit Simulation Cmd* to obtain the dialog box on the right.

Select *AC Analysis* and set:

Type of Sweep = Linear
Number of Points = 300
Start Frequency = 10k
Stop Frequency = 25k

These settings are also displayed on the schematic diagram.

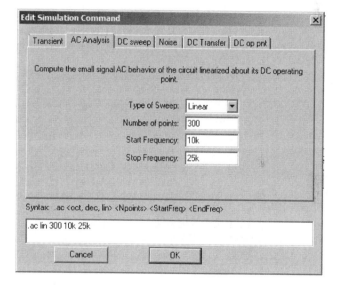

A plot window will appear after the simulation is run. Move the cursor to the output node (Vo) and left click when the voltage probe appears. The Bode magnitude and phase response will be graphed in the plot window.

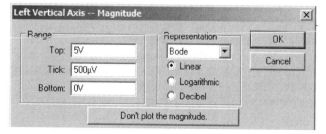

Click on the plot window. The vertical and horizontal axis settings can be edited by moving the mouse to each axis and left clicking.

The Bode plot below shows a resonant frequency of about 16 KHz and a bandwidth of about 3200 Hz. The phase angle is 0 degrees at the resonant frequency, 45 degrees at the lower cut-off frequency, and -45 degrees at the upper cut-off frequency.

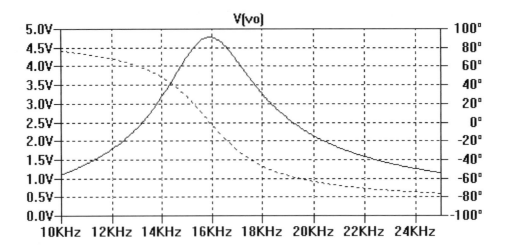

Vo and θ as a Function of Frequency

PSpice Example: Series RLC Circuit Frequency Response

The circuit below was used to plot the frequency responses of two series resonant circuits. The two circuits are identical except the top one has a series resistance of 920 Ω while the bottom one has a series resistance of 460 Ω. This way the responses of the two circuits may be compared. The Q of the second circuit is twice the first. Note the resulting difference in the bandwidth of the two circuits in the graph below on the right.

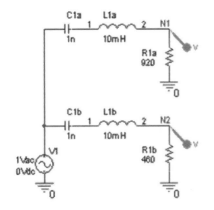

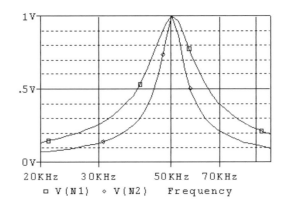

AC sweep is set to vary the analysis frequency from 20 KHz to 100 KHz. Sweep is logarithmic with 50 points per decade. Values for the resonant frequency and bandwidth may be obtained from the "*Probe*" graphs by using the "cursors". You can "zoom" in on the graphs by adjusting the plot's x-axis in Probe.

Experiment 39: Parallel Resonant Band-Pass Filter

Introduction

Determining the effect of inductor winding resistance is somewhat more difficult in a parallel resonant circuit. However, the effect on the circuit's quality factor, Q, and bandwidth, BW, can be approximated by converting the series resistance of the inductor winding to an equivalent parallel resistance.

Parallel Resonance

A simple parallel RLC circuit is shown on the right. As with the series RLC circuit, its resonant frequency, f_0, can be calculated by setting X_L equal to X_C:

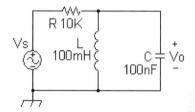

$$f_0 = \frac{1}{2\pi\sqrt{LC}} = 1592\,Hz.$$

The circuit's quality factor, Q, as defined by the ratio of the energy stored to the energy dissipated per cycle, is R/X_L, where X_L is the reactance of the inductor at the circuit's resonant frequency.

A series-parallel RLC circuit is shown on the right. R_W is the winding resistance of the inductor. Consider the loop consisting of R_W, L, and C as a series resonant circuit.

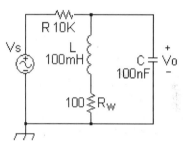

Calculate the loops resonant frequency and use the result to calculate the impedance of the series combination of R_W and L: $\mathbf{Z} = R_W + \mathbf{j}\,X_L$. Transform $\mathbf{Z}$ into a parallel equivalent circuit:

$$\mathbf{Y} = \frac{1}{\mathbf{Z}} = \frac{1(R_W - \mathbf{j}X_L)}{(R_W + \mathbf{j}X_L)(R_W - \mathbf{j}X_L)} = \frac{(R_W - \mathbf{j}X_L)}{R_W^2 + X_L^2} = \frac{R_W}{R_W^2 + X_L^2} - \mathbf{j}\frac{X_L}{R_W^2 + X_L^2}$$

Next convert the components of the admittance into components of parallel impedance:

$$R_P = \frac{R_W^2 + X_L^2}{R_W} \qquad X_P = \frac{R_W^2 + X_L^2}{X_L} \qquad L_P = \frac{X_P}{2\pi f_0}$$

The series-parallel circuit may be converted to an entirely parallel circuit by also converting the voltage source in series with R to a current source in parallel with R, as shown on the right.

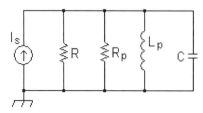

151

The circuit's Q and bandwidth can now be calculated from the parallel equivalent circuit:

$$Q = \frac{R \parallel R_P}{X_P} = \frac{R R_P}{2\pi f_0 L_P (R + R_P)} \qquad BW = \frac{f_0}{Q} \qquad \text{(note that usually } L_P \approx L)$$

Objectives

The measured response of the parallel RLC circuit will be compared to analysis and simulation. Two important parameters, resonant frequency, f_0, and bandwidth, BW, will be measured.

Procedure

Equipment and Parts

Function Generator, Oscilloscope with 10X probes, Breadboard.
Inductor: 100 mH, 5%, Capacitor: 0.1μF, 5%.
Resistors: R = 10 KΩ, ¼ watt, 5%.

Resonant Frequency and Bandwidth

1. Measure and record the resistance of the resistor, R, and inductor, Rw. If possible, measure the inductance of the inductor and capacitance of the capacitor

   R _____   Rw _____

   L _____   C _____

2. Connect C, L, and R together with no wires in between. Connect the generator and oscilloscope leads directly to the components.

3. Set channel 1 of the oscilloscope to measure Vs. Set channel 2 to measure Vo. Set the oscilloscope to trigger on channel 1.

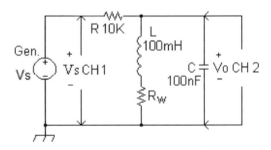

4. Set the function generator to produce a 5 V, peak-to-peak, 1600Hz sine wave, with no offset (this is Vs). Adjust the generator to the frequency where Vo is maximum. This will occur at the circuit's resonant frequency, f_0.

5. Measure and record the frequency, f_0, and the peak to peak value of the voltage, Vo. Also measure and record the phase angle, θ_0.

   f_0 _____   Vo(max) _____ θ_0 _____

6. Adjust the generator to a frequency below f_0 where Vo is 0.707 of its maximum value. Measure the phase angle of Vo. Record the frequency as f_1, and the angle as θ_1.

   f_1 _____ Vo(-3dB) _____ θ_1 _____

7. Adjust the generator to a frequency above f_0 where Vo is 0.707 of its maximum value. Measure the phase angle of Vo. Record the frequency as f_2, and the angle as θ_2.

   f_2 _____ Vo(-3dB) _____ θ_2 _____

Analysis

1. Organize your data into a spreadsheet. Use your measured part values.

	A	B	C	D	E	F	G	H	I	J
1	Measured					Simulated				
3		Freq. Hz	Vo p-p	Vo Deg.			Freq. Hz	Vo p-p	Vo Deg.	% Error
4	Fo					Fo				
5	F1					F1				
6	F2					F2				
7	BW					BW				

2. Transfer your measured results into the table. Calculate the theoretical values of the resonant frequencies and cutoff frequencies. Enter the results into the table.

3. Enter equations into the appropriate cells to calculate BW and percent error.

4. Simulate the circuit to check the results of your calculations. Refer to the simulation example below.

PSpice Example: Parallel Resonant Circuit

Use "AC Sweep" analysis to plot the magnitude and phase response of the circuit. Use your measured component values.

Note in the graph below that the horizontal axis is linear and expanded between 1 KHz and 2 KHz so that the frequencies, f_0, f_1, and f_2, could be determined more accurately.

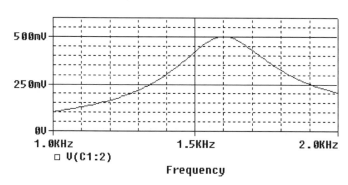

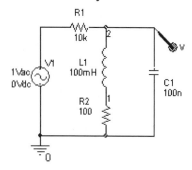

153

Experiment 40: Two-Pole Low-Pass Filter

Introduction

A low pass filter's ability to attenuate signals whose frequencies are above f_C improves when the filters are "cascaded".

Figure A on the right shows a simple, cascaded, two pole-low pass "passive" filter. The circuit in Figure B on the right uses the same two filter sections as the circuit in Figure A.

In Figure B, the filters are separated by a "buffer" op-amp, so that they don't interact with each other. The op-amp's input impedance is very high so that it does not load down the filter, and its output impedance is close to zero ohms. The frequency response of the two circuits will be investigated and compared.

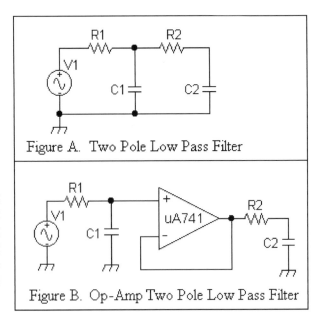

Figure A. Two Pole Low Pass Filter

Figure B. Op-Amp Two Pole Low Pass Filter

Passive Filter

It is somewhat difficult to calculate the transfer function of the passive multi-pole filter. This is simplified for Figure A by setting R1 = R2 = R and C1 = C2 = C.

$$H(S) = \frac{1/(RC)^2}{s^2 + 3/(RC)s + 1/(RC)^2} \qquad H(j\omega) = \frac{1/(RC)^2}{\left(1/(RC)^2 - \omega^2\right) + j\omega\left(3/(RC)\right)}$$

The cutoff frequency is found by setting the magnitude of this transfer function equal to $1/\sqrt{2}$.

$$|H(j\omega)| = \frac{1/(RC)^2}{\sqrt{\left(1/(RC)^2 - \omega^2\right)^2 + (3\omega/RC)^2}} = \frac{1}{\sqrt{2}}$$

Cutoff frequency: $\qquad \omega_C = 0.374/RC \qquad f_C = 0.0595/RC$

Op-Amp Filter

Op-amp filters are called "active" filters. The op-amp buffer between the two-low pass filter sections makes it easier to calculate the transfer function of the two pole filter in Figure B. Its transfer function is the product of the transfer function of each section.

154

$$H(s) = \frac{1/RC}{(s+1/RC)} \frac{1/RC}{(s+1/RC)} = \frac{(1/RC)^2}{s^2 + (2/RC)s + (1/RC)^2}$$

$$H(j\omega) = \frac{(1/RC)^2}{\left((1/RC)^2 - \omega^2\right) + j\omega(2/RC)} \qquad \omega_c = \frac{0.6434}{RC} \qquad f_c = \frac{0.1024}{RC}$$

Objectives

The frequency response of the passive 2-pole low-pass filter and the active 2-pole low-pass filter will be measured and compared.   Results will be compared to theoretical expectations

Procedure

Equipment and Parts

Function Generator, Oscilloscope, Power Supply, Breadboard.
LM741 / uA741 op-amp. Two 4.7 KΩ, ¼ watt resistors.
Two 10 nF, 5%, polyester film capacitors.

Part 1: Without a Buffer

1.   Measure the values of the parts.

       R1 _____   R2 _____   C1 _____   C2 _____

2.   Connect the circuit on the right.   Connect the function generator and oscilloscope channel 1 to Vs, the input of the circuit. Connect oscilloscope channel 2 to Vo, the output of the   circuit.

3.   Set channels 1 and 2 of the oscilloscope to 2 V/DIV.
        Set the time base to 20 mS/DIV and set the trigger to channel 1, positive slope.

4.   Set the function generator to produce a 10 V peak-to-peak, 10 Hz, sine wave. Two cycles should be observed on both channels of the oscilloscope. Channel 2 amplitude should be about the same as channel 1 (10 V peak-to-peak).

5.   The next objective is to generate a table of filter output voltages at various frequencies. The amplitude of the function generator must remain constant (10 V peak-to-peak) at all frequencies. The output amplitude should be measured as accurately as possible by adjusting channel 2 to obtain the largest display.

       Use the channel switch on the oscilloscope to switch between channels 1 and 2 when making these measurements. Measure the output voltage at the following frequencies: 10, 100, 500, and 1000 Hz.

155

6. Measure the frequencies where the output is 7.07 V, 5.00 V, 1.00 V, and 0.100 V.

7. Record your measurements into spreadsheet columns A and B.

A suggested layout is given on the right.

	A	B	C	D	E
1	Frequency	Output		Frequency	Output
2	Hertz	Volts		Hertz	Volts
4	10			10	
5	100			100	
6	500			500	
7	1000			1000	
8		7.07			7.07
9		5.00			5.00
10		1.00			1.00
11		0.10			0.10

Part 2: With a Buffer

1. Connect the circuit on the right. Connect the function generator and oscilloscope channel 1 to the input of the circuit (Vs).

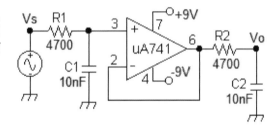

2. Connect oscilloscope channel 2 to Vo, the output of the circuit. Repeat steps 3 through 6 of part 1.

2. Record your measurements into spreadsheet columns D and E.

Optional design exercise: Design a two-pole low-pass filter using an op-amp buffer with a cutoff frequency of 400 Hz and a minimum input impedance of 22 KΩ. Test your design by simulation and write a short report on the results.

Analysis, Part 1

1. Use the spreadsheet to plot the frequency response of the filter. Set the x-axis and the y-axis on the spreadsheet plot to "log".

2. Use the slope of the plot for frequencies one decade beyond the cutoff frequency to determine the filter's attenuation in units of dB per decade.

3. Calculate the filter's theoretical cutoff frequency. Calculate the percent difference between the theoretical and measured cutoff frequencies.

4. Simulate the circuits using your measured component values. Compare the simulated and calculated cutoff frequencies. They should be the same. Compare the measured and simulated attenuation in dB per decade.

Analysis, Part 2

1.   Use the spreadsheet to plot the frequency response of the filter. Set the x-axis and the y-axis on the spreadsheet plot to "log".

2.   Use the slope of the plot for frequencies one decade beyond the cutoff frequency to determine the filter's attenuation in units of dB per decade.

3.   Calculate the filter's theoretical cutoff frequency. Calculate the percent difference between the theoretical and measured cutoff frequencies.

4.   Simulate the circuits using your measured component values. Compare the simulated and calculated cutoff frequencies. They should be the same. Compare the measured and simulated attenuation in dB per decade.

5.   Compare the results of part 1 and part 2.

PSpice Example: Two-Pole Low Pass Filter

The response of a two-pole passive low-pass filter is compared to a two-pole active low-pass filter.

The active filter has an op-amp buffer between the two sections. Section 1 is composed of R1 and C1. Section 2 is composed of R2 and C2.

The passive filter is composed of R3-C3 and R4-C4.

Both filters are connected to a 1 V AC source, V3, which is swept from 10 Hz to 3000 Hz.

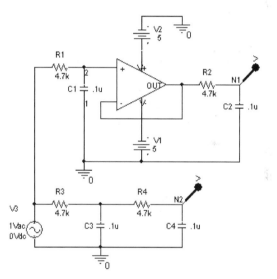

The plot shows that the cutoff frequency of the active circuit is higher than the cutoff frequency of the passive circuit. Also, the slope of the response above the cutoff frequency is greater for the active filter. Both axis are set to "LOG".

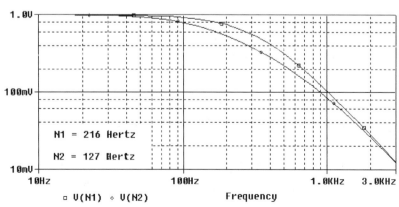

157

Experiment 41: Active Two-Pole Low-Pass Butterworth Filter

Introduction

A Butterworth unity gain low-pass filter frequency response is given by the equation:

$$|H(j\omega)| = \frac{1}{\sqrt{1 + (\omega/\omega_c)^{2n}}}$$, where ω_c is the cutoff frequency and n is the order of the filter.

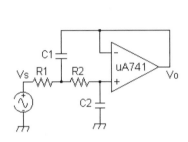

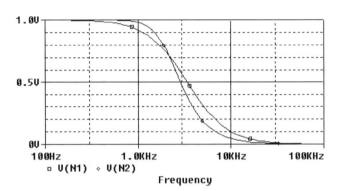

A second order low-pass Butterworth filter circuit is shown above. Its frequency response, V(N2), is compared to the frequency response, V(N1) of the cascaded second order filter in the previous lab experiment (40). The Butterworth filter has a much flatter response in the pass band and more attenuation beyond the cutoff frequency.

If R1 is set equal to R2, the transfer function of the second order Butterworth filter is:

$$H(s) = \frac{\left(1/R^2\,C1C2\right)}{s^2 + (2/RC1)s + \left(1/R^2\,C1C2\right)}. \quad If\ R1 = R2 = R\ \ and\ \ C1 = 2C2,\ \ \omega_c = \frac{1}{\sqrt{2}RC2}.$$

Higher order Butterworth filters can be designed by cascading filter sections using the appropriate "Butterworth polynomials" to calculate the part values required for each section.

Objectives

The frequency response of a two pole active low-pass Butterworth filter will be measured. The results will be compared to theoretical calculations and to simulation.

Procedure

Equipment and Parts

Power supply, Oscilloscope, Function Generator, DMM, Breadboard.
Resistors: Two 4.7 KΩ, ¼ watt, 5%. Capacitors: 10 nF, 20 nF, 5% (or 11 nF and 22 nF)
Operational Amplifier: LM741 or equivalent.

---

1.   Measure and record the values of your parts.

      R1 _____   R2 _____   C1 _____   C2 _____

2.   Connect the circuit on the right. Connect the generator and oscilloscope channel 1 to Vs. Connect oscilloscope channel 2 to Vo.

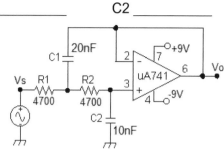

3.   Set channels 1 and 2 of the oscilloscope to 2 V/DIV. Set the time base to 20 mS and set the trigger to channel 1, positive slope.

4.   Set the function generator to produce a 10 V peak-to-peak, 10 Hz, sine wave. Two cycles should be observed on both channels of the oscilloscope. Channel 2 amplitude should be about the same as channel 1 (10 V peak-to-peak).

5.   Generate a table of filter output voltages at specified frequencies. Amplitude of the generator must remain constant at all frequencies. Measure the output amplitude as accurately as possible by using the largest oscilloscope wave form display.

      Use the channel switch on the oscilloscope to switch between channels 1 and 2 when making measurements. Measure the output voltage at the following frequencies: 10, 100, 500, and 1000 Hz.

      Measure the frequencies where the output is 7.07 V, 5.00 V, 1.00V, and 0.100V.

6.   Record your measurements into spreadsheet columns A and B. Suggested layout is given on the right.

7.   Optional: Design a third order Butterworth filter whose cutoff frequency is the same as this lab's two pole filter. Refer to your textbook.

	A	B
1	Frequency	Output
2	Hertz	Volts
4	10	
5	100	
6	500	
7	1000	
8		7.07
9		5.00
10		1.00
11		0.10

Analysis

1.   Use the spreadsheet to plot the frequency response of the filter. Set the x-axis and the y-axis on the spreadsheet plot to "log".

2.   Use the slope of the plot for frequencies one decade beyond the cutoff frequency to determine the filter's attenuation in units of dB per decade.

3.   Calculate the filter's theoretical cutoff frequency. Calculate the percent difference between the theoretical and measured cutoff frequencies.

4.   Simulate the circuits using your measured component values. Compare the simulated and calculated cutoff frequencies. They should be the same. Compare the measured and simulated attenuation in dB per decade.

Experiment 42: Active Band-Pass Filter

Introduction

The operational amplifier band-pass filter circuit on the right uses a high-pass and a low-pass filter section to obtain a band-pass response.

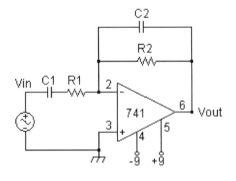

The RC network, R2 and C2, in its negative feedback path provides the low-pass portion of the band-pass response.

Series connected C1 and R1 provide the high- pass portion.

This circuit has a typical second order resonant response of the form:

$$H(s) = \frac{Ks}{s^2 + \beta s + \omega_o^2} \qquad \beta = bandwidth \qquad \omega_o = resonant\ frequency$$

Using the node voltage method to solve for the circuit's transfer function:

$$\frac{0-Vin}{R1 + \frac{1}{sC1}} + \frac{0-Vout}{R2} + \frac{0-Vout}{\frac{1}{sC2}} = 0 \qquad H(s) = \frac{-s\dfrac{1}{C2R1}}{s^2 + s\left(\dfrac{1}{C1R1} + \dfrac{1}{C2R2}\right) + \left(\dfrac{1}{C1R1}\right)\left(\dfrac{1}{C2R2}\right)}$$

$$H(j\omega) = \frac{-j\omega K\omega_2}{\left(\omega_o^2 - \omega^2\right) + j\omega\left(\omega_1 + \omega_2\right)} \qquad K = \frac{R2}{R1} \qquad \omega_1 = \frac{1}{C1R1} \qquad \omega_2 = \frac{1}{C2R2} \qquad \omega_o^2 = \omega_1\omega_2$$

$$\text{Gain when } \omega = \omega_o : A_V = \frac{K\omega_2}{\left(\omega_1 + \omega_2\right)}$$

It is important to note that the bandwidth of this filter is the sum of the cutoff frequencies of the individual sections: $\beta = \omega_1 + \omega_2$, and not $\omega_2 - \omega_1$.

The bandwidth does approach the traditional definition of bandwidth, $\beta = \omega_2 - \omega_1$, when the cutoff frequencies are over a decade apart.

The actual cutoff frequencies are the frequencies where the magnitude of the filter's transfer function is equal to -3 dB of its maximum value. The theoretical values of these frequencies are most easily found by simulation. Solutions using Maple are also provided in the analysis section of this experiment.

Objectives

The frequency response of a wide-bandwidth and narrow-bandwidth active band-pass filter will be measured and the results will be compared to theoretical expectations.

Procedure

Equipment Required

Function Generator, Oscilloscope, Power Supply, Breadboard.
Capacitors: 1 nF, 10 nF, 100 nF, 5%.
Op-Amp: LM741, Resistors: 10 KΩ, 12 KΩ, 5%, ¼ watt.

Part 1: Narrow Bandwidth

1. Measure the values of the parts. If possible, measure the values of the capacitors.

   R_{10k} _____ R_{12k} _____ C_{1nF} _____ C_{10nF} _____ C_{100nF} _____

2. Connect the circuit on the right. Connect the function generator to Vin. Connect channel 1 of the oscilloscope to Vin and channel 2 to Vout. Set the trigger to channel 1.

3. Set the function generator to produce a 5 KHz, 1 V peak-to-peak sine wave with no offset.

4. Adjust the function generator frequency to produce the maximum output voltage, Vout, on channel 2.

   Record the value of the voltage, Vout, and the frequency, fo

   Vout _____ volts p-p   fo _____

5. Decrease the function generator frequency to a frequency, f1, below fo where the magnitude of Vout is 0.707 of its maximum value. Record the frequency f1 below.

   Increase the function generator frequency to a frequency, f2, above fo where the magnitude of Vout is 0.707 of its maximum value. Record the frequency f2 below.

   f1 _____   f2 _____

Part 2: Wide Bandwidth

1. This procedure is the same as part 1, except change the value of C1 to 100nF.

2. Adjust the function generator frequency to produce the maximum output voltage, Vout, on channel 2. Record the value of the voltage, Vout, and the frequency, fo.

   Vout _____ volts p-p   fo _____

3. Decrease the function generator frequency to a frequency, f1, below fo where the magnitude of Vout is 0.707 of its maximum value in step 2 above. Record the frequency f1 below.

Increase the function generator frequency to a frequency, f2, above fo where the magnitude of Vout is 0.707 of its maximum value in step 2 above. Record the frequency f2 below.

f1 _____   f2 _____

Analysis, Part 1

1. Calculate the maximum output voltage and theoretical cutoff frequencies of the filter. Calculate the percent difference between the calculated and measured results.

2. Simulate the circuit and compare your calculated results to the simulated results.

Analysis, Part 2

1. Calculate the maximum output voltage and theoretical cutoff frequencies of the filter. Calculate the percent difference between the calculated and measured results.

2. Simulate the circuit and compare your calculated results to the simulated results.

3. Compare the filter's bandwidth using $BW = f_2 - f_1$ and $BW = f_1 + f_2$, using the theoretical cutoff frequencies for each filter section.

4. Simulate the circuit and compare your calculated results to the simulated results

Maple Example: Frequency and Bandwidth Calculations

Given: $w1 = 1/R1C1$ and $w2 = 1/R2C2$. $K = R2/R1$. Calculations below are for $w1 = 10$ and $w2 = 100$. Input w1 and w2 for your filter. Maple will calculate the filter's cutoff frequencies.

```
> restart;
> w1:=10.0;w2:=100.0;
w1 := 10.0
w2 := 100.0
> fc1:=abs(.5*(-w1-w2+(w1^2+w2^2+6*w1*w2)^.5))/6.283;
fc1 := 1.343766942
> fc2:=abs(.5*(-w1-w2-(w1^2+w2^2+6*w1*w2)^.5))/6.283;
fc2 := 18.85132702
> Amax := w2/(w1+w2);
Amax := .9090909091
> BW:=fc2-fc1;
BW := 17.50756008
> BW2:=(w1+w2)/6.283;
BW2 := 17.50756008
```

162

LTspice Example: Simulation of Active Band-Pass Filter

This simulation uses the generic "opamp" in the opamp library. It is easy to use and requires no power supply connections. The directive, ".lib opamp.sub" must be added. Click on "op" on the right side of the main menu bar and type in the directive. It will be displayed on the schematic as shown below.

This simulation analysis was set to "AC Analysis", decade sweep, 50 points per decade, start frequency = 100, and stop frequency = 100,000.

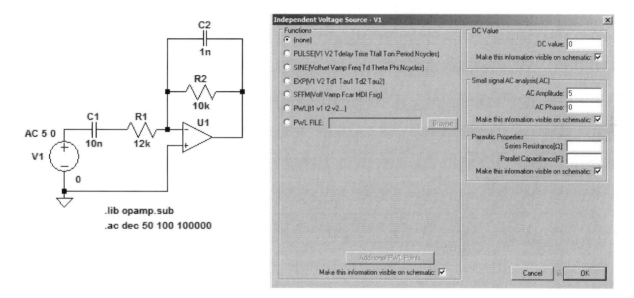

Right click on the voltage source to open the above dialog box. AC amplitude is set to 5, DC value is set to 0, and AC phase is set to 0. Move the mouse over the plot to read the x-y coordinates of the cursor at the bottom of the screen.

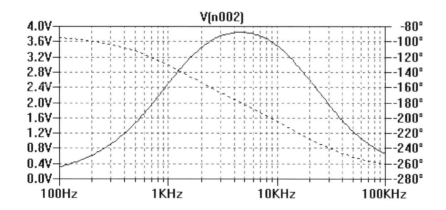

163

Experiment 43: Resonant Band-Stop Filter

Introduction

Band-stop filters are used to block or trap undesired frequencies. Band-stop filters are often used in conjunction with band-pass to reduce the possibility of interference in communications systems and instrumentation amplifiers.

The block diagram on the right shows the basic concept. Three configurations may be considered. Z1 could be a resistance and Z2 could be a series resonant circuit. Z2 could be a resistance and Z1 could be a parallel resonant circuit. Z1 could be a parallel resonant circuit and Z2 could be a series resonant circuit.

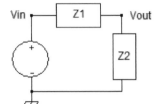

Series resonant circuit: $Z_s = sL + \dfrac{1}{sC} + R_w = \dfrac{s^2 + s\dfrac{R_w}{L} + \dfrac{1}{LC}}{s\dfrac{1}{L}}$.

Parallel resonant circuit: $Z_p = \dfrac{1}{\dfrac{1}{sL} + \dfrac{1}{Q^2 R_w} + sC} = \dfrac{s\dfrac{1}{C}}{s^2 + s\dfrac{1}{Q^2 R_w C} + \dfrac{1}{LC}}$

R_W is the resistance of the inductor. It is approximated as its parallel equivalent, $Q^2 R_W$, above.

Filter transfer functions for Z1 = R and Z2 = Z_S:

$$H(s) = \frac{s^2 + s\dfrac{R_w}{L} + \dfrac{1}{LC}}{s^2 + s\left(\dfrac{R_w + R}{L}\right) + \dfrac{1}{LC}} \qquad H(j\omega) = \frac{\left(\omega_0^2 - \omega^2\right) + j\omega \dfrac{R_w}{L}}{\left(\omega_0^2 - \omega^2\right) + j\omega\left(\dfrac{R_w + R}{L}\right)}$$

Filter transfer functions for Z1 = Z_P and Z2 = R:

$$H(s) = \frac{s^2 + s\dfrac{1}{Q^2 R_w C} + \dfrac{1}{LC}}{s^2 + s\left(\dfrac{1}{Q^2 R_w C} + \dfrac{1}{RC}\right) + \dfrac{1}{LC}} \qquad H(j\omega) = \frac{\left(\omega_0^2 - \omega^2\right) + j\omega\left(\dfrac{1}{Q^2 R_w C}\right)}{\left(\omega_0^2 - \omega^2\right) + j\omega\left(\dfrac{1}{Q^2 R_w C} + \dfrac{1}{RC}\right)}$$

Objectives

This experiment will investigate the characteristics of two band-stop filter configurations. In part 1, Z1 is a resistor and Z2 is a series resonant circuit whose impedance is Z_S. In part 2, Z2 is a resistor and Z1 is a parallel resonant circuit whose impedance is Z_P.

Procedure

Equipment and Parts

Function Generator, Oscilloscope, Breadboard.
Capacitor: 10 nF, 5%. Inductor: 100 mH, 5%. Resistors: 1 KΩ, 10 KΩ, 5%, ¼

Part 1: Series Resonant

1. Measure the values of the parts including inductor resistance R_W. L and C if possible.

    R_{1k} _____ R_{10k} _____ R_W _____ L _____ C _____

2. Connect the circuit on the right. Connect the oscilloscope to channel 1 to measure Vs and channel 2 to measure Vo. Set the trigger to channel 1.

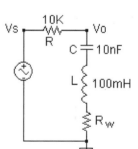

3. Set the function generator to produce a 10 V peak-to-peak sine wave, with no offset, at a frequency of 5 KHz.

4. Carefully adjust the generator's frequency to obtain the lowest output voltage, Vo, on channel 2 (it should be near 5 KHz). Record the voltage, Vo, and frequency, fo.

    Vo _____ volts p-p fo _____

5. Tune the function generator to frequencies lower than fo, where the output voltage Vo has the following peak-to-peak voltage values: 2.0, 5.0, 7.07, 8.4, and 9.7. Be sure to keep the voltage, Vs, on channel 1 at exactly 10.0 V p-p. Record in the table below.

Volts p-p	f below fo		Volts p-p	f above fo
2.0			2.0	
5.0			5.0	
7.07			7.07	
8.4			8.4	
9.7			9.7	

6. Tune the function generator to frequencies higher than fo, where the output voltage Vo has the following peak-to-peak voltage values: 2.0, 5.0, 7.07, 8.4, and 9.7. Be sure to keep the voltage, Vs, on channel 1 at exactly 10 V p-p. Record in the table above.

165

7.   Change the value of the resistor, R, to 1 KΩ. Carefully adjust the generator's frequency to obtain the lowest output voltage, Vo, on channel 2 (it should be near 5 KHz). Record the voltage, Vo, and frequency, fo.

Vo _____ volts p-p   fo _____

8.   Repeat steps 5 and 6 above and record results into the table below.

Volts p-p	f below fo		Volts p-p	f above fo
2.0			2.0	
5.0			5.0	
7.07			7.07	
8.4			8.4	
9.7			9.7	

Part 2: Parallel Resonant

1.   Connect the circuit on the right. Connect oscilloscope channel 1 to measure Vs and channel 2 to measure Vo. Set the trigger to channel 1.   Set the function generator to produce a 5 KHz, 10 V p-p sine wave, with no offset.

2.   Carefully adjust the generator's frequency to obtain the lowest output voltage, Vo, on channel 2 (it should be near 5 KHz). Record the voltage, Vo, and frequency, fo.

Vo _____ volts p-p   fo _____

3.   Tune the function generator to frequencies lower than fo, where the output voltage Vo has the following peak-to-peak voltage values: 2.0, 5.0, 7.07, 8.4, and 9.7. Be sure to keep the voltage, Vs, on channel 1 at exactly 10.0 V. Record in the table below.

Volts p-p	f below fo		Volts p-p	f above fo
2.0			2.0	
5.0			5.0	
7.07			7.07	
8.4			8.4	
9.7			9.7	

4.   Tune the function generator to frequencies higher than fo, where the output voltage Vo has the following peak-to-peak voltage values: 2.0, 5.0, 7.07, 8.4, and 9.7. Be sure to keep the voltage, Vs, on channel 1 at exactly 10.0 V. Record in the table above.

5.   Change the value of the resistor, R, to 1K.   Carefully adjust the generator's frequency to obtain the lowest output voltage, Vo, on channel 2 (it should be near 5 KHz). Record the voltage, Vo, and frequency, fo.

Vo _____ Volts p-p   fo _____

6.   Repeat steps 3 and 4 above and record results into the table below.

Volts p-p	f below fo		Volts p-p	f above fo
2.0			2.0	
5.0			5.0	
7.07			7.07	
8.4			8.4	
9.7			9.7	

Analysis, Part 1

1.   Calculate the band-stop resonant frequency and the minimum output voltage. Express the filter's maximum attenuation in dB. Calculate the percent difference between the calculated values and the measured results.

2.   Simulate the circuit and compare your calculated results to the simulated results (they should be in close agreement). Compare the -3dB bandwidth of the simulated filter to your measurement.

Analysis, Part 2

1.   Calculate the band-stop resonant frequency and the minimum output voltage. Express the filter's maximum attenuation in dB. Calculate the percent difference between the calculated values and the measured results.

2.   Simulate the circuit and compare your calculated results to the simulated results (they should be in close agreement). Compare the -3dB bandwidth of the simulated filter to your measurement.

PSpice Example: Parallel–Series Resonant Band-Stop Filter

The value of R1 in the simulation below was optimized to produce the response shown. Change the value of R1 to 1k and 10k to see what the un-optimized response looks like.

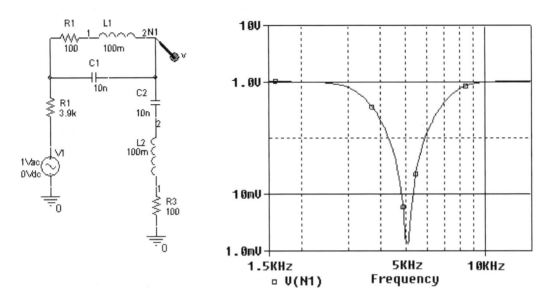

An attenuation of about 60 dB is indicated by the frequency response plot above.

$$dB = 20\log\left(\frac{1mV}{1000mV}\right) = -60$$

The same amount of attenuation may be achieved with the single resonant circuit filters by changing the value of the series resistor. For example, using the series resonant circuit would require the value of the series resistor to be 100,000 ohms. However, the -3 dB bandwidth of the circuit would be much greater (try it).

Another way to improve the frequency response would be to use a higher Q inductor. For example, replace the one with a 100 Ω series resistance with one that has a 10 Ω series resistance. However, this inductor would be physically larger and more expensive.

Experiment 44: Fourier Series and Circuit Analysis

Introduction

According to Fourier analysis, a square wave may be considered to be a superposition of an infinite number of odd harmonic frequencies whose amplitudes decrease inversely with frequency. The fundamental is the lowest frequency of the square wave. The Fourier series of a square wave voltage, whose peak-to-peak amplitude is V, and average value is V_{AVE}, may be expressed as:

$$v(t) = V_{AVE} + \frac{2V}{\pi} \sum_{n}^{\infty} \frac{1}{n} \sin(2\pi n f_0 t),$$

where n is an odd integer and f_0 is the fundamental frequency.

If a square wave is applied to a filter circuit, the wave's frequency components will be affected by the filter's frequency response. The filter's output frequency spectrum will be different than the input frequency spectrum.

Although the Fourier series of any time domain waveform consists of an infinite number of harmonic frequencies, an adequate approximation may be obtained using only the first several terms of the series. The average value plus the first 5 terms for the square wave are:

$$v(t) = V_{AVE} + \frac{2V}{\pi} \sin(2\pi f_0 t) + \frac{2V}{3\pi} \sin(6\pi f_0 t) + \frac{2V}{5\pi} \sin(10\pi f_0 t) + \frac{2V}{7\pi} \sin(14\pi f_0 t) + \frac{2V}{9\pi} \sin(18\pi f_0 t)$$

Fourier analysis may be used to calculate the frequency response of a filter to a square wave input. First the magnitude and phase angle of each frequency component of the square wave is calculated. Next the transfer function of the filter is calculated for each frequency component. Then the output of the filter at each frequency is calculated as the phasor product of the input at that frequency and the filter's transfer function at that frequency.

An example is presented here for the filter circuit on the right. The input, Vg, is a 2-volt peak-to-peak, 100Hz square wave with a 1-volt offset. The first 4 terms of the Fourier series for Vg are:

$$v_g(t) = 1 + 1.273 \sin(2\pi 100t) + .424 \sin(2\pi 300t) + .255 \sin(2\pi 500t)$$

The transfer function of the filter is: $T_f = \dfrac{Vo}{Vg} = \dfrac{1}{1 + j\dfrac{f}{88.3}}$.

Its magnitude is: $|T_f| = \dfrac{1}{\sqrt{1 + \left(\dfrac{f}{88.3}\right)^2}}$. Its phase angle is: $\theta = -\arctan(\dfrac{f}{88.3})$.

The values of the transfer function of the filter in phasor form for each frequency, DC, 100Hz, 300Hz, and 500Hz are:

$V_{DC} = 1$, $\quad$ $V_{100} = .662\angle-48.56$, $\quad$ $V_{300} = .282\angle-73.6$, $\quad$ $V_{500} = .174\angle-80.0$.

The output of the filter can now be calculated:

$V_{DC}=1(1)$, $\quad$ $V_{100}=(1.273\angle0^0)(.662\angle-48.56^0)$, $\quad$ $V_{300}=(.424\angle0^0)(.282\angle-73.6^0)$,

$V_{500}=(.255\angle0^0)(.174\angle-80.0^0)$

$v_o(t) = 1 + .843\sin(2\pi100t - 48.56^0) + .120\sin(2\pi300t - 73.6^0) + .044\sin(2\pi500t - 80.0^0)$

Compare the above results to the simulation below.
Note: Display at least 4 cycles of the waveform before applying the FFT. The FFT is obtained by clicking on the FFT button in the main menu.

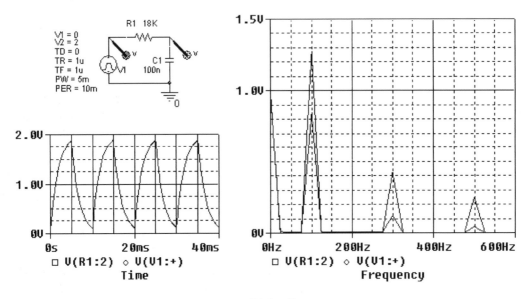

Objectives

The frequency response of a low-pass filter to a square wave input will be calculated for the fundamental, third harmonic, and fifth harmonic frequencies of the square wave. These sinusoidal frequencies will be applied to the filter, and the filter's response at each frequency will be measured. The results will be compared to a simulation using the Fast Fourier Transform (FFT).

Procedure

Equipment and Parts
Function Generator, Oscilloscope, and Breadboard. Resistor: 15 KΩ, ¼ watt, 5%. Capacitor: 100 nF, 5%.

1. Connect the circuit on the right. Connect the oscilloscope channel 1 to node N1 and channel 2 to node N2.

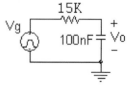

2. Vg is the function generator set to produce a 120 Hz, 3 V peak-to-peak, square wave with a 1.5 V offset (goes between 0 and 3 V).

3. Observe the time domain waveform on channel 2. Capture or sketch about 2 cycles of the output waveform. Indicate the amplitude, offset, and period of the waveform.

4. Calculate the magnitude of the input, Vg, at 120Hz, 360Hz, and 600Hz, using the Fourier series for the square wave. Verify your calculations by simulation using the FFT (refer to this experiment's introduction). Record in the table below.

Frequency	Calculated Mag. Vg Volts-peak	Measured Mag. Vo Volts-peak	Measured Angle Vo Degrees
120			
360			
600			

5. Set the function generator to produce a sine wave at each frequency of the same magnitude as calculated in step 4 above. Measure and record the peak magnitude and phase angle of the output, Vo, at each frequency. Record in the table above.

Analysis

1. Calculate the transfer function of the filter as a phasor for DC, 120Hz, 360Hz, and 600Hz.

2. Calculate the output of the filter at each frequency using phasor analysis.

3. Compare the magnitude of the measured output, Vo, with the calculated output at each frequency. Calculate the percent difference between the measured and calculated results.

4. Compare the measured phase angle of the output, Vo, with the calculated phase angle of the output at each frequency. Calculate the percent difference between the measured and calculated results.

5. Simulate the circuit. Use the FFT feature of PSpice to display the magnitude of the first four terms of the output of the filter and compare the simulated results to the calculated results.

Note: Set the time domain display to about 4 cycles. Change the frequency axis of the FFT to display 0 to 800Hz. Simulated output magnitudes are in volts-peak.

Experiment 45: Band-Pass Filter / FFT / Square Wave

Introduction

According to Fourier analysis, a square wave may be considered to be a superposition of an infinite number of odd harmonic frequencies whose amplitudes decrease inversely with frequency. The fundamental is the lowest frequency of the square wave. The Fourier series of a square wave voltage, whose peak-to-peak amplitude is V, and average value is V_{AVE}, may be expressed as:

$$v(t) = V_{AVE} + \frac{2V}{\pi} \sum_{n}^{\infty} \frac{1}{n} \sin(2\pi n f_0 t), \text{ where n is an}$$

odd integer and the fundamental frequency is f_0.

If a square wave is applied to a band-pass filter, the wave's frequency components will be affected by the filter's frequency response. The filter's output frequency spectrum will be different than the input frequency spectrum.

In Fourier analysis, the concepts of "time-domain" and "frequency-domain" are important to understand. The square wave input to the filter and output from the filter are considered to be expressed in the time-domain when amplitude is expressed as a function of time.

An oscilloscope normally plots waveforms in the time-domain. When the amplitude of the waveform is expressed as a function of frequency, it is expressed in the frequency-domain.

Using Fourier analysis, it is possible to convert time-domain expressions into the frequency-domain, and frequency-domain expressions into the time domain. This may be done by a computer algorithm called the "Fast Fourier Transform", or "FFT", which is built into many analysis software packages, including *OrCAD PSpice*.

Although the Fourier series of any time-domain waveform consists of an infinite number of harmonic frequencies, an adequate approximation may be obtained using only the first several terms of the series. This exercise will involve the average value of the series plus the first 3 harmonics. These are:

$$v(t) = V_{AVE} + \frac{2V}{\pi} \sin(2\pi f_0 t) + \frac{2V}{3\pi} \sin(6\pi f_0 t) + \frac{2V}{5\pi} \sin(10\pi f_0 t)$$

Objectives

The FFT feature of the Tektronix TDS oscilloscope will be used to display and measure the response of a band-pass filter to a square wave input. The results will be compared to theoretical calculations.

One objective of this experiment is to investigate the relationship between time-domain analysis and frequency-domain analysis. Acquired time-domain data will be compared to simulation data using *OrCAD PSpice*.

Procedure

Equipment and Parts

Function Generator, Digital Oscilloscope with FFT, and Breadboard.
Resistors: 3.3 KΩ, 18 KΩ, ¼ watt, 5%.
Capacitors: 1 μF (non-polarized), 100 nF, 5%.

1. Connect the circuit on the right. Connect the oscilloscope channel 1 to node N1 and channel 2 to node N2.

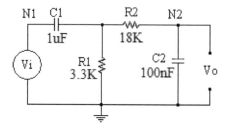

2. Vi is the function generator set to produce a 20 Hz, 2 V peak-to-peak, square wave with a 1 V offset (goes between 0 and 2 V).

3. Set the oscilloscope to display 10 cycles of the input and output waveforms as shown below.

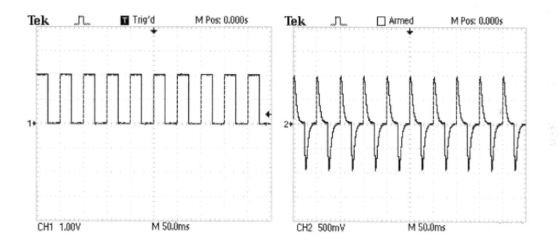

It may be helpful to read the section on displaying the Fourier spectrum of your instrument's user manual.

The TDS1002 uses a "Math FFT" algorithm to generate the Fourier spectrum from the acquired time-domain data. The time-domain waveform needs to be set up carefully to get an accurate display of the spectrum. Please note the following:

a. The FFT spectrum is calculated from the center 2048 points of the time-domain waveform. Since there are 2500 points in the 10 divisions of the entire display, the FFT is calculated from about the center 8 divisions.

b. There is a tradeoff between frequency resolution and the bandwidth of the displayed spectrum (due to aliasing).

173

c.	The highest frequency (and bandwidth) that can be measured accurately by a digitizing oscilloscope is one half the sample rate (the Nyquist frequency).

d.	The TDS1002 transforms 2048 time-domain points to 1024 frequency-domain points resulting in a spectrum whose bandwidth is equal to the Nyquist frequency.

e.	The amplitude is displayed in dB where 0 dB is equal to 1 V rms.

$$dB_{VRMS} = 20\log\frac{V_{RMS}}{1Vrms} \ .$$

f.	Use the cursors to determine the amplitudes of the harmonics.

g.	Use data capture such as the TekXL toolbar for greater accuracy.

4.	To obtain the FFT spectrum of channel 1: Push the "MATH MENU" button, select "FFT", set the MATH FFT source to channel 1.

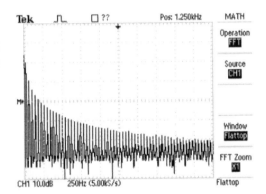

Note the resulting display on the right.
The frequency scale is 250Hz/Div.
The amplitude scale is in dB, where
0 dB = 1 V rms.

5.	The frequency scale needs to be expanded by a factor of 10 in order to accurately measure the frequency components. This could be done with the time base (SEC/DIV) control. However, this would reduce the bandwidth from 2500 Hz to 250 Hz. The TDS1002 has an FFT zoom control that provides a zoom up to 10. A zoom factor of 10 was used to obtain the input (CH1) and output (CH2) frequency spectrums shown below.

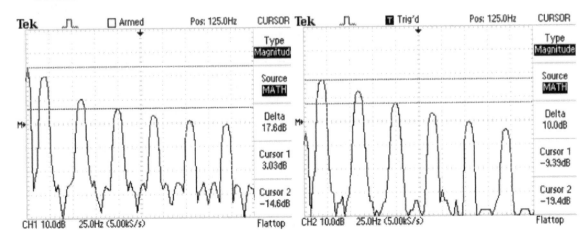

174

Cursors should be used to measure the amplitudes. The input frequency spectrum (channel 1) above shows an rms amplitude value of 3 dB at 0 Hz. This corresponds to 1.414 V rms, which is equal to a 1 V average value (DC offset). The fifth harmonic at 100 Hz has an amplitude of −14.6 dB. This corresponds to a peak voltage of 0.254 V. The output frequency spectrum shows the fifth harmonic amplitude to be −19.4 dB.

6. Display the first six harmonics of the input and output spectra of your band pass filter. Record the amplitude of the DC component and the first three harmonics of the input and output spectra (DC, 20 Hz, 60 Hz, 100 Hz).

Vi_{DC} _____dBV Vi_{20} _____dBV Vi_{60} _____dBV Vi_{100} _____dBV

Vo_{DC} _____dBV Vo_{20} _____dBV Vo_{60} _____dBV Vo_{100} _____dBV

Analysis

Note: Use a spreadsheet as applicable to do the analysis below.

1. The Fourier series of the input waveform is that of a 2 V peak-to-peak amplitude square wave with a 1.0 V DC component (average value). Determine the theoretical magnitude of the waveform's DC component, fundamental, third harmonic and fifth harmonic. Convert your calculated results to dBV using the following equation:

$$dBV = 20\log\frac{Vrms}{1Vrms}.$$

Compare your measured values to the theoretical values by calculating the percent difference between them.

2. Simulate the filter circuit with *OrCAD PSpice* and use the FFT feature of *Probe* to obtain the frequency spectrum of the output. Compare the simulated results to your calculated results from step 1 above. See PSpice example on the next page.

3. Simulate the circuit with *OrCAD PSpice* and use the frequency sweep analysis to obtain a Bode Plot of the filter's response (similar to plot shown below). Compare the results to analysis steps 2 and 3 above.

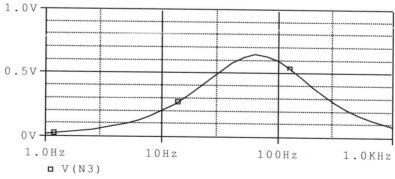

175

PSpice Example: Fourier Analysis / Square Wave

It is easy to obtain the frequency spectrum of a time-domain waveform in *OrCAD PSpice*. There is an FFT button in the main menu of Probe that converts the time-domain display to frequency-domain. Display about 5 to 10 cycles of the waveform to get good resolution in the frequency-domain.

The waveforms and spectrum shown below are for the simulation of a band-pass filter circuit. The square wave is generated by the part "VPULSE".

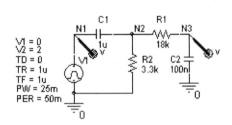

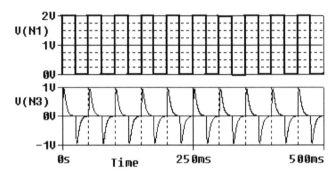

Filter Circuit

The spectrum displayed in the Probe window is a plot of the peak voltage at each harmonic frequency.

To convert these voltages to dBV apply the following equation:

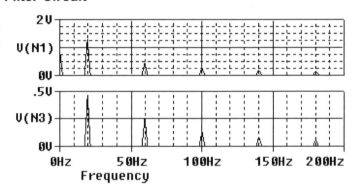

$$dBV = 20\log(\frac{V_{PEAK}}{\sqrt{2}})$$

For example, the output spectrum shows 0.47 volts at 20Hz and 0.26 volts at 100Hz.

$$dBV_{20HZ} = 20\log(\frac{.47}{\sqrt{2}}) = -9.57 \text{, and } dBV_{100HZ} = 20\log(\frac{.15}{\sqrt{2}}) = -19.5 \text{.}$$

Experiment 46: Band-Pass Filter / FFT / Triangle Wave

Introduction

According to Fourier analysis, a triangle wave may be considered to be a superposition of an infinite number of odd harmonic frequencies whose amplitudes decrease inversely with frequency. The fundamental frequency is the lowest frequency of the triangle wave. The Fourier series of a triangle wave voltage, whose peak-to-peak amplitude is V, and average value is V_{AVE}, may be expressed as:

$$v(t) = V_{AVE} - \frac{4V}{\pi^2} \sum_{n}^{\infty} \frac{1}{n^2} \cos(2\pi n f_0 t),$$

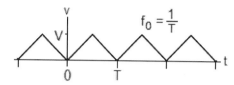

where n = odd, and the fundamental frequency is f_0.

If a triangle wave is applied to a band-pass filter, the wave's frequency components will be affected by the filter's frequency response. The filter's output frequency spectrum will be different than the input spectrum.

Compared to the square wave, the amplitude of the harmonics of a triangle wave decrease much more rapidly with frequency. The Fourier series for the average plus the first three terms is:

$$v(t) = V_{AVE} + \frac{4V}{\pi^2} \cos(2\pi f_0 t) + \frac{4V}{9\pi^2} \cos(6\pi f_0 t) + \frac{4V}{25\pi^2} \cos(10\pi f_0 t).$$

Objectives

The FFT feature of the Tektronix TDS oscilloscope will be used to display and measure the response of a band-pass filter to a triangle wave input. The results will be compared to theoretical calculations.

Procedure

Equipment and Parts
Function Generator, Digital Oscilloscope with FFT, and Breadboard. Resistors: 3.3K, 18K, ¼ watt, 5%. Capacitors: 1uF (non-polarized), 100nF, 5%.

1. Connect the circuit on the right. Connect the oscilloscope channel 1 to node N1 and channel 2 to node N2.

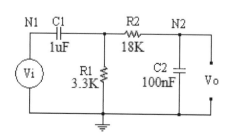

2. Vi is the function generator set to produce a 20 Hz, 2 V peak-to-peak, triangle wave with a 1 V offset (goes between 0 and 2 V).

3. Set the oscilloscope to display 10 cycles of the input and output waveforms. Refer to the previous experiment for information on using the Tektronix TDS1002 oscilloscope's FFT function.

4. Display the first six harmonics of the input and output spectra of your band pass filter. Record the amplitude of the DC component and the first three harmonics of the input and output spectra (DC, 20 Hz, 60 Hz, 100 Hz).

Vi_{DC} _____ dB Vi_{20} _____ dB Vi_{60} _____ dB Vi_{100} _____ dB

Vo_{DC} _____ dB Vo_{20} _____ dB Vo_{60} _____ dB Vo_{100} _____ dB

Analysis

Note: Use a spreadsheet as applicable to do the analysis below.

1. The Fourier series of the input waveform is that of a 2 V peak-to-peak amplitude triangle wave with a 1.0 V DC component (average value). Determine the theoretical magnitude of the waveform's DC component, fundamental, third harmonic and fifth harmonic. Convert your calculated results to dBV using the following equation:

$$dBV = 20 \log \frac{Vrms}{1Vrms}.$$

Compare your measured values to the theoretical values by calculating the percent difference between them.

2. Simulate the filter circuit with *OrCAD PSpice* and use the FFT feature of *Probe* to obtain the frequency spectrum of the output. Compare the simulated results to your calculated results from step 1 above. See PSpice example below.

PSpice Example: Fourier Analysis / Triangle Wave

The triangle waveform in PSpice is generated by the part "PPWL_RE_FOREVER". To set the frequency and amplitude you first need to double click on the part to open the property editor. Locate the columns "FIRST_NPAIRS", "SECOND_NPAIRS", and "THIRD_NPAIRS". Enter the times and magnitudes as shown below to generate a 20 Hz triangle wave which goes between 0 V and 2 V repetitively.

Source Part				
VPWL_RE_FOREVER.Normal				
FIRST_NPAIRS	SECOND_NPAIRS	THIRD_NPAIRS	TSF	VSF
0,0	25m,2	50m,0		

178

Ten cycles of the triangle wave are shown below with the resulting output of the filter below it. Note that the output looks like a slightly distorted sine wave.

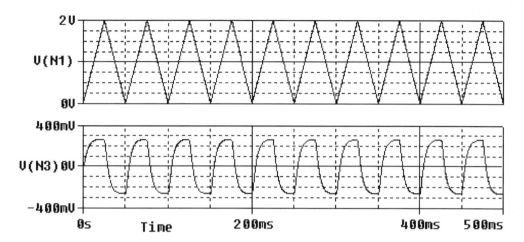

Note that the triangle wave has a much closer resemblance to a sine wave than the square wave. The triangle wave's harmonics decrease in amplitude as the inverse square of the frequency.

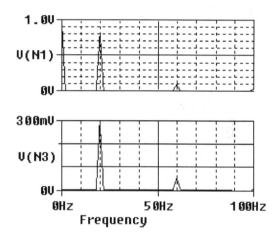

Experiment 47: Two-Port Networks / Z Parameters

Introduction

A two-port network is an electrical circuit or device with two input terminals (input port) and two output terminals (output port). Two port network analysis deals with the relationship between the network's input and output voltages and currents as related to the network's parameters such as its impedance or admittance.

This exercise focuses on a network's impedance, Z, parameters.

$$Z_{11} = \frac{V_1}{I_1}\bigg|_{I_2=0} \quad Z_{12} = \frac{V_1}{I_2}\bigg|_{I_1=0} \quad Z_{21} = \frac{V_2}{I_1}\bigg|_{I_2=0} \quad Z_{22} = \frac{V_2}{I_2}\bigg|_{I_1=0}$$

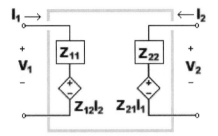

$$\begin{bmatrix} V_1 \\ V_2 \end{bmatrix} = \begin{bmatrix} Z_{11} & Z_{12} \\ Z_{21} & Z_{22} \end{bmatrix} \begin{bmatrix} I_1 \\ I_2 \end{bmatrix}$$

Input impedance and output impedances are given by:

$$Z_{in} = Z_{11} - \frac{Z_{12}Z_{21}}{Z_{22} + Z_L} \qquad Z_{out} = Z_{22} - \frac{Z_{12}Z_{21}}{Z_{11} + Z_S}$$

Z_L is the load impedance connected to port 2. Z_S is the source impedance connected to port 1.

Objectives

The parameters of a resistor ladder network will be measured and analyzed in part 1 of this exercise. Part 2 is a "black box" exercise. The port parameters will be used to determine the required value of load impedance for each network. The impedance match will be verified using the maximum power transfer theorem.

Procedure

Equipment and Parts
DC Power Supply, DMM, and Breadboard. Resistors: 1K, 1.5K, 2.2K, 3.3K, 4.7K, all ¼ W, 5%. 10K trim pot.

Part 1: Resistor Ladder

1.	Measure the values of your resistors (refer to diagram below).

R1 _____ R2 _____ R3 _____ R4 _____ R5 _____

2.   Connect the circuit on the right.

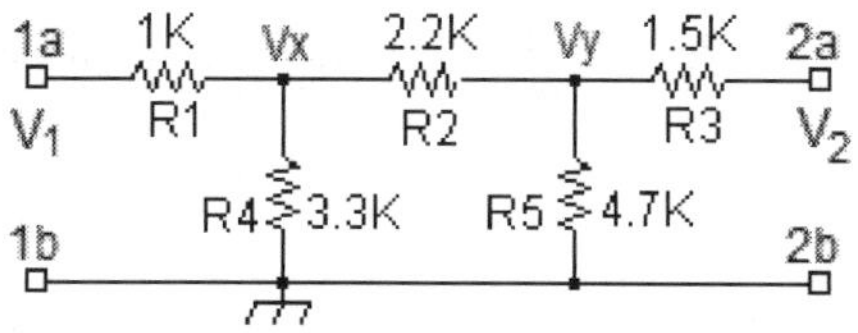

3.   Measure and record the resistance, R_{11}, between terminals 1a and 1b.

        R_{11} _____

4.   Measure and record the resistance, R_{22}, between terminals 2a and 2b.

        R_{22} _____

5.   Connect the positive of a 10 V DC source to terminal 1a and the negative to terminal 1b. Measure and record the voltage, V_2, across the terminals 2a and 2b. Measure and record Vx.

        V_2 _____   Vx _____

6.   Connect the positive of a 10 V DC source to terminal 2a and the negative to terminal 2b. Measure and record the voltage, V_1, across the terminals 1a and 1b. Measure and record Vy.

        V_1 _____   Vy _____

7.   Connect the positive of a 10 V DC source to terminal 1a and the negative to terminal 1b. Connect the DMM to terminals 2a and 2b.

        Set the DMM to measure current. Use the DMM's highest current range that gives a 3 decimal place display.   Record the "short circuit" current.

        I_{SHORT} _____

8.   Set the DMM to measure voltage.   Measure and record the "open circuit" voltage.

        V_{OPEN} _____

9.   Connect a 10K potentiometer across terminals 2a and 2b and adjust its resistance so that the voltage across it is exactly one half of the open circuit voltage. Record the voltage across the potentiometer.

        V_{POT}: _____

181

Part 2: Black Box Network

The instructor will give you a black box resistor network with the input terminals marked 1a and 1b, and the output terminals marked 2a and 2b, as shown below.

The black boxes should have 3 to 5 resistors whose values are between 1K and 10K, and output impedance between 2K and 8K ohms.

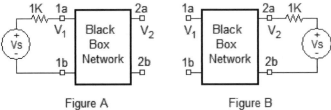

Figure A   Figure B

1. Connect the circuit in Figure A. Set Vs to 10 V DC.   Measure and record V_1 across the terminals 1a and 1b.   Measure and record V_2 across the terminals 2a and 2b.

    V_1 _____ V_2 _____ .

2. Connect the circuit in Figure B. Set Vs to 10 V DC. Measure and record V_1 across the terminals 1a and 1b Measure and record V_2 across terminals 2a and 2b.

    V_1 _____ V_2 _____

3. Connect 10 volts DC between terminals 1a (positive) and 1b (negative). Connect the DMM to terminals 2a and 2b. Set DMM to measure current. Use the highest current range that gives a 3 decimal place display. Record the "short circuit" current.

    I_{SHORT} _____

4. Set the DMM to measure voltage. Measure and record the "open circuit" voltage.

    V_{OPEN} _____

5. Connect a 10K potentiometer across terminals 2a and 2b and adjust its resistance so that the voltage across it is exactly one half of the open circuit voltage. Remove the potentiometer from the circuit and measure its resistance (resistance between the two terminals that were connected to terminals 2a and 2b).   Record the resistance.

    R_{POT} _____

Analysis, Part 1

1. Calculate the circuit's Z parameters using measured values of the resistors, R1 to R5.

2. Use the measurements in steps 5 and 6 to calculate the circuit's Z parameters. Z_{11} should be very close to the measured value of R_{11} in procedure step 3. Similarly, Z_{22} should be very close to the measured value of R_{22} in procedure step 4.

182

3. Calculate the circuit's theoretical output impedance using the Z parameters calculated in step 1 above (input impedance, $Z_S = 0$): $Z_{out} = Z_{22} - \dfrac{Z_{12}Z_{21}}{Z_{11} + Z_S}$.

4. Calculate the circuit's theoretical output impedance using the measured Z parameters calculated in step 2 above (input impedance, $Z_S = 0$).

5. Calculate the percent difference between the calculated theoretical output impedance in step 3 and the measured output impedance in step 4.

6. Calculate the percent difference between the theoretical output impedance and the measured resistance of the potentiometer in procedure step 5.

7. Calculate circuit's output resistance using measurements in procedure steps 7 and 8. Calculate percent difference between theoretical and measured output impedance.

8. Optional: Simulate the circuit to compare the measured voltages to the simulated voltages. Refer to PSpice example below.

Analysis, Part 2

1. Use the measurements in steps 1 and 2 to calculate the circuit's Z parameters.

2. Calculate the circuit's output impedance using the Z parameters calculated in step 1 above (input impedance, $Z_S = 0$).

3. Calculate the percent difference between the output impedance calculated in analysis step 2 and the measured resistance of the potentiometer in procedure step 5.

4. Calculate the circuit's output resistance using the measurements in procedure steps 3 and 4. Calculate the percent difference between this output impedance and that calculated in analysis step 2.

PSpice Example: Resistor Ladder Analysis

The simulation below was done using the "Bias Point" simulation setting. The 10 meg resistor, R6, represents the internal resistance of the DMM.

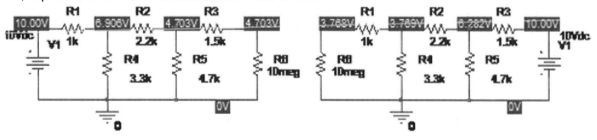

The simulation on the next page was done using the "DC Sweep" simulation setting. R6 was varied from 10 Ω to10 KΩ in 10 Ω steps.

To vary the value of R6, get the part "PARAM" from the special library. Double click on "PARAMETER". In the properties dialog box, set ""Filter by" to "OrCad-PSpice". Click on "New Column", name it Rx and set Rx to 1K.

On the schematic, double click on the value of R6 and change it to "{Rx}". Be sure to include the curly brackets as shown on the diagram below.

The graph shows that maximum power occurs when the value of Rx is about 3.3K ohms (1.6 mW).

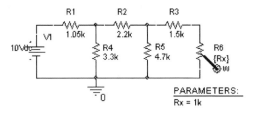

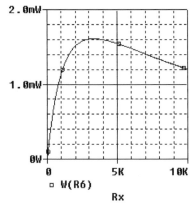

LTspice Example: Resistor Ladder Analysis

Draw the Circuit

In this simulation, the value of R6 is varied from 10 Ω to 10,000 Ω in 10 Ω steps. R6's value is indicated as "{Rx}" on the schematic.

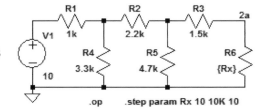

Setup the Analysis

Spice directives can be entered directly into the schematic by pressing the letter "s". Enter the directives ".*op*" and ".*step param RX 10 10K 10*" and place them in a convenient place on the schematic.

Simulate the Circuit

Run the simulation. To plot the power dissipation of R6, click in the plot window, click on "*Plot Settings*" in the main menu, select "*Add trace*", type V(a2)*-I(R5). Click ok.

The plot below shows that maximum power occurs for a value of R6 of about 3300 ohms.

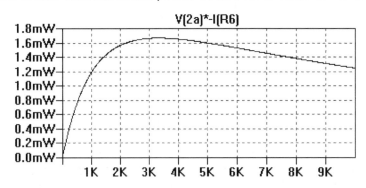

184

Experiment 48: Measuring Capacitance and Inductance

Introduction

In circuit analysis we often assume that we have ideal components. An ideal resistor has only the property of resistance, which is independent of frequency. In reality, a resistor also has the properties of inductance and capacitance, but these properties are not significant at low frequencies. Experiments in this manual are purposely done at frequencies below 10 KHz so that the values and properties of the components will be relatively independent of frequency. A good quality digital multi-meter can read resistor values with an accuracy of better than 1%.

Instruments are available which can measure capacitance accurately. Inductance, however, is difficult to measure accurately even at low frequencies. Inductors have wire resistance and capacitance, and the inductance also depends on the frequency and current.

One purpose of doing the experiments in this manual is to gain confidence in the theoretical foundation of circuit analysis. We want to know that the circuit performance will be as predicted by the theoretical analysis. In order to compare the measured results to theory, we need to know the values and properties of the components used. Resistance can be measured accurately with the DMM. Capacitance and inductance values will be determined by AC measurements and phasor analysis.

Capacitance Measurement

The circuit and phasor diagrams used for determining the capacitor's value are shown on the right.

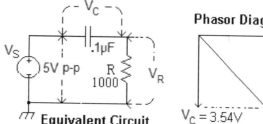

Since the current, I, in all of the components of the series circuit is the same, $V_C = I \, X_C$, and $V_R = I \, R$.

In the diagram above, $\mathbf{V_S}$ is set to 5 volts peak-to-peak, and to the frequency, f_C, where $|V_C| = |V_R|$. At that frequency $X_C = R$.

R can be measured with an ohmmeter and C can be calculated:

$$X_C = R = \frac{1}{2\pi f_C \, C} \text{ , therefore } C = \frac{1}{2\pi f_C \, R} \text{ .}$$

Inductance Measurement

At low frequencies an inductor may be approximated by an inductance in series with a resistance. The resistance is mainly due to the wire winding of the inductor. This resistance does increase with frequency, but it is approximately constant for the low frequencies used in the experiments in this manual.

185

The diagrams below shows the equivalent circuit and phasor diagrams used for determining the inductance of the inductor. Note that we can't directly measure the voltage across R_W (inductor wire resistance), but we can measure the voltage across R_X. We can use the voltage V_X across R_X to determine the voltage V_R across both resistances, $(R_X + R_W)$.

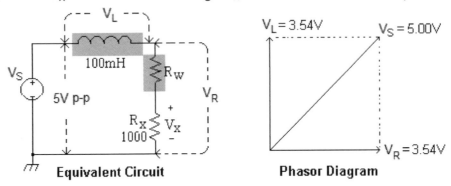

| Equivalent Circuit | Phasor Diagram |

V_S is set to 5 volts peak-to-peak and to the frequency, f_C, where $X_L = (R_X + R_W)$. At that frequency $|V_L| = |V_R|$ and $X_L = (R_X + R_W)$. X_L can be calculated:

$$X_L = 2\pi f_C L = (R_W + R_X).$$

V_R can't be directly measured. Its required value is determined from the measurement of V_x:

$$V_x = \frac{R_X}{R_X + R_W} V_R \quad \text{and} \quad L = \frac{(R_W + R_X)}{2\pi f_C}.$$

Objectives
This is primarily an inductance and capacitance measurement exercise. If an accurate inductance and capacitance measurement instrument is available, the results may be compared to its measurements.

Procedure

Equipment and Parts

Function Generator, Oscilloscope with 10X probes, Breadboard.
L = 100 mH, 30mA, Mouser Xicon 43LJ410 or equivalent.
C = 0.1 µF, 5%, capacitor, polyester film. R = 1000 ohms, 5%, ¼ watt.

Procedure Part 1: Capacitance Measurement

Measure the value of the 1000 Ω resistor, Rx, and record below. If you have a capacitance meter, measure the value of the 0.1µF capacitor and record below.

Rx _____   C _____

2. Connect the circuit on the right.

R_{th} is the internal resistance of the function generator and V_{th} is the open circuit voltage of the function generator.

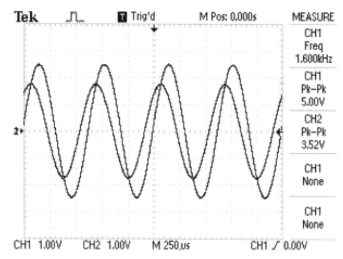

3. With the circuit connected, set the generator to produce a 5.00 V peak-to-peak amplitude sine wave with no offset on channel 1 of the oscilloscope at a frequency of 1600 Hz.

4. Carefully vary the function generator frequency, f_C, while observing the amplitude of the voltage, V_C, on channel 2 of the oscilloscope.

Adjust the frequency so that $|V_C|$ is exactly 3.54 V peak to peak. Check that the channel 1 voltage is exactly 5 V peak-to-peak. If not, reset it to 5 V peak-to-peak and re-adjust the frequency to get 3.54-volts peak to peak on channel 2. At this frequency, f_C, the magnitude of the capacitive reactance equals the value of the resistance, R_x. Also measure and record the phase angle, θ_C of channel 2 with respect to channel 1. Calculate and record the capacitance:

$$C = \frac{1}{2\pi f_C R_x}$$ $C = $ _____ $\theta_C = $ _____

Note the display on the right. The oscilloscope's "measure" feature was used to display the frequency and amplitudes on the right side of the screen.

(Refer to your oscilloscope's user manual)

Also note the phase shift between channel 1 and channel 2. Channel 2 leads channel 1 by 45 degrees.

5. If you measured the capacitance with a capacitance meter in step 1, compare that measurement to the result of step 4 of this procedure. If the difference is greater than 3%, either the meter is inaccurate, or there is an error in the procedure of step 4.

6. The results of step 4 should be accurate to about 3% when using an oscilloscope.

Procedure Part 2: Inductance Measurement

1. Use the same 1000 Ω resistor, R_X, which you used in part 1. Measure the resistance, R_W, of the inductor with a DMM. If you have an inductance meter, measure and record the value of the 100 mH inductor below.

    R_W: _____   L: _____

2. Connect the circuit on the right.

    Set the function generator to produce a 5 V peak-to-peak amplitude sine wave with no offset on channel 1 of the oscilloscope at a frequency of 1600 Hz.

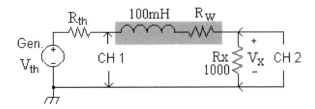

    The reactance of the inductor will be equal to the resistance (R_X + R_W) when the voltage across (R_X + R_W) is equal to 3.54 volts peak-to-peak.

    Calculate and record the magnitude of V_X: $V_X = \dfrac{R_X}{R_X + R_W} 3.54$.

    V_X = _____

3. Vary the function generator frequency while observing the amplitude of the voltage, V_X, on channel 2 of the oscilloscope. Adjust the frequency so that V_X is exactly equal to the voltage calculated above (channel 1 voltage must be exactly 5 V peak-to-peak). At this frequency, f_C, the inductive reactance equals the resistance of (R_X + R_W). Measure and record the phase angle θ_X of channel 2 with respect to channel 1. Calculate the inductance (use measured values of R_X and R_W):

    $$L = \frac{(R_X + R_W)}{2\pi f_C}. \quad L = \underline{\hspace{3cm}} \quad \theta_X = \underline{\hspace{3cm}}$$

4. If you measured the inductance with an inductance meter, compare that measurement to the results of step 3 of this procedure. If the difference is greater than 3%, either the meter is inaccurate, or there is an error in the procedure of step 3.

5. The results of step 3 should be accurate to about 3% when using an oscilloscope.

Analysis

1. Calculate the percent difference between the measured component values and the labeled component values.

2. Simulate the circuits in parts 1 and 2 at the same frequencies you used in the lab exercise. Use the measured values of your components. Compare the output voltages to those you measured. Compare the simulated phase angles. Write a short report expressing the results of the experiment and the simulation.

Experiment 49: Frequency Response Plot

Introduction

A Tektronix TDS oscilloscope, such as the TDS1002, is capable of plotting the frequency response of a circuit network over a range of two decades.

This procedure requires a function generator capable of generating a frequency sweep and an oscilloscope with data logging capability connected to a computer. The procedure in this part was done with an Agilent 33120A function generator, a Tektronix TDS1002 oscilloscope, a PC with Microsoft Excel, and Tek Open Choice software.

Objectives

The frequency response of a series resonant RLC filter will be plotted using the frequency sweep capability of a function generator and the data logging capability of an oscilloscope.

Procedure

Equipment and Parts

Function Generator with frequency sweep capability and Breadboard.
Oscilloscope with 10X probes and data logging capability.
L = 100 mH, 5%, Mouser Xicon 43LJ410 or equivalent.
C = 0.1 μF, 5%, capacitor, polyester film. R = 220 ohms, 5%, ¼ watt.

---

1. Measure the value of the inductor's resistance. R_W _____

    Connect the circuit on the right.

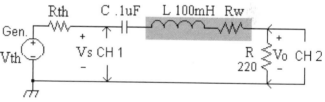

2. Open Excel. You should see the TekXL tool bar. Click on "connection".

3. Select an instrument, usually the first one, and click on "identify". The instrument ID should appear at the bottom of the window, in this case, "TDS1002".

    Click "OK".

    If there is a problem with this part of the procedure, you may need to ask the instructor or lab assistant for help.

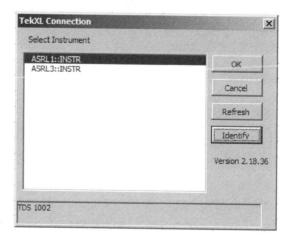

189

4.   Click on "Measurements" in the TekXL tool bar to open widow below.

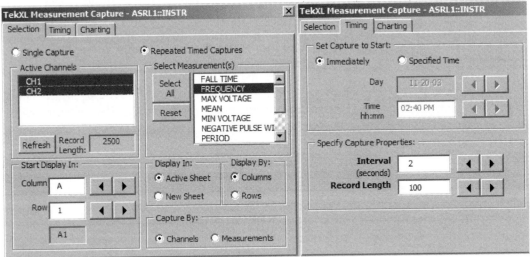

Click the "Selection" tab and select both channels 1 and 2.   Select the measurements: FREQUENCY and ROOT MEAN SQUARE. Click on the "Timing" tab.

5.   Timing settings depend on the capability of the function generator and oscilloscope interface.   The example frequency response plot shown on the next page was done using an Agilent 33120A function generator set to produce a logarithmic sweep from 1 KHz to 100 KHz in 400 seconds.

If you need help setting the function generator, ask the lab instructor or assistant. You can also refer to the function generators user manual.

The sampling interval was set to 2 seconds so one would expect 200 measurements in 400 seconds. However, only 95 measurements were actually made in that time, due to a slow serial interface. So the record length was set to 100. Set the timing according to the capability of your oscilloscope's interface.

6.   The oscilloscope time base needs to be set so that one cycle is displayed at the lowest frequency, in this case, 100 µS/Div.   At the highest frequency there will be 100 cycles displayed.

Since the oscilloscope takes 2500 samples per screen, one cycle of 1000 Hz would consist of 2500 samples and one cycle of 100KHz would consist of 25 samples.

7.   Set the function generator to produce a 1-volt rms sine wave.   Set both vertical channels of the oscilloscope to 500mV/DIV.   You should now be ready to start the sweep.

8.   The Agilent function generator starts the sweep when the "Single/TRIG" button is pressed. TekXL Measurement starts when the start button is clicked.   Click the start button first, then immediately push the "Single/TRIG" button on the function generator.

Observe the frequency increase on the oscilloscope screen and in Excel. Channel 2 frequencies will be way off initially due to the low amplitude of the channel 2 signal. Stop the acquisition at 100KHz. You can delete the channel 2 frequency column and format the columns for better readability. See the sample result on the next page.

Sample Acquisition

The first 35 of 95 rows of the measurements are shown below. The columns and graphs have been formatted. The dip in the function generator output at the resonant frequency in the first graph is due to the generator's internal resistance.

Plotting the "Transfer Function" of the filter can eliminate this effect. This was done in the second graph by plotting ratio of the filter's output to its input.

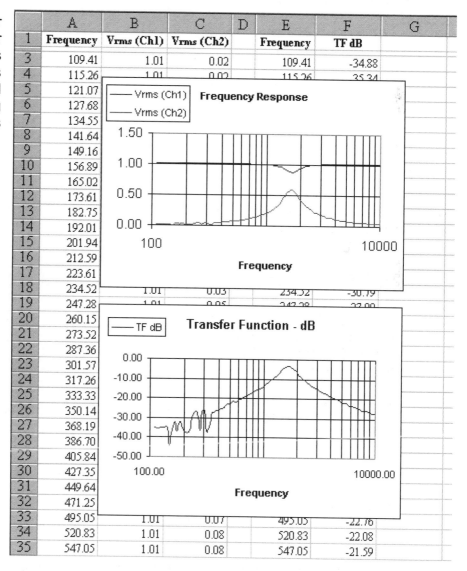

	A	B	C	D	E	F	G
1	Frequency	Vrms (Ch1)	Vrms (Ch2)		Frequency	TF dB	
3	109.41	1.01	0.02		109.41	-34.88	
4	115.26	1.01	0.02		115.26	35.34	
5	121.07						
6	127.68						
7	134.55						
8	141.64						
9	149.16						
10	156.89						
11	165.02						
12	173.61						
13	182.75						
14	192.01						
15	201.94						
16	212.59						
17	223.61						
18	234.52	1.01	0.03		234.52	-30.79	
19	247.28	1.01	0.05		247.28	27.00	
20	260.15						
21	273.52						
22	287.36						
23	301.57						
24	317.26						
25	333.33						
26	350.14						
27	368.19						
28	386.70						
29	405.84						
30	427.35						
31	449.64						
32	471.25						
33	495.05	1.01	0.07		495.05	-22.76	
34	520.83	1.01	0.08		520.83	-22.08	
35	547.05	1.01	0.08		547.05	-21.59	

Cell F3 has the equation: =20*LOG10(C3/B3). Writing "=(C3/B3)" in cell F3 would generate a linear plot.

Analysis

1. Simulate the RLC circuit with P*Spice*. Use "AC Sweep" analysis to plot the magnitude and phase response of the circuit from 100 Hz to 10,000 Hz. See below. Be sure to use your measured component values.

2. Use the cursors in *PSpice* to locate fo, f1, and f2 on the *PSpice* plot.

3. Note the circuit and simulation results on the right and the simulation settings below.

4. Eliminate the internal resistance effect by plotting the ratio of the output voltage to the input voltage, V(R:2)/V(R2:2) in this example.

You can also change the vertical scale to log if desired.

5. Compare your simulation results with your calculations. They should be in close agreement.

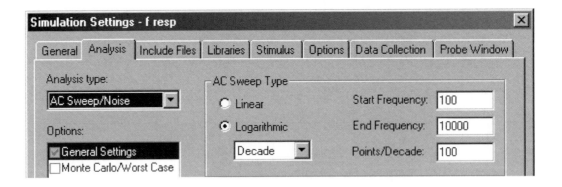

192

Appendix

A1: Electric Circuits Lab Report Information

Introduction

The purpose of the laboratory is threefold. First is to learn how to use typical laboratory instruments to make a variety of measurements. Second is to reinforce the lecture material by demonstrating practical applications of electric circuit theory. Third is to learn how to analyze data and write a lab report.

Each laboratory experiment will involve several, and possibly all, of the following skills. You should be able to use a word processor and a spreadsheet such as Microsoft Word and Excel. You will learn all the other skills listed below.

1. How to connect electrical circuits using a circuit diagram.
2. How to measure voltage, current, and resistance.
3. How to collect and record data.
4. How to present data in lab a report.
5. How to simulate electric circuits using circuit simulation software.

The Lab Station

A typical electronic lab station consists of the following instruments: power supply, digital multi-meter, function generator, frequency counter, oscilloscope, computer, and computer data acquisition equipment and software.

A solder-less breadboard, or prototyping board, is used to connect the circuits. The instruments are connected to the breadboard as needed. **As a general rule, it is best to use the smallest number of wires, and the smallest number of connections, when doing an experiment. This reduces the number of things that can go wrong, and it is easier to see how everything is connected.**

Many people must use the laboratory and its equipment, so it is important that everyone using the lab cooperates in keeping it in good condition. At the end of each lab period you are responsible for straightening up your lab station.

Make sure that all the equipment is turned off, unless told otherwise. Remove all loose papers and disposable items (loose wires, paper clips, etc.). Test equipment leads should be restored to their proper positions. Report any equipment malfunctions or other problems to your instructor or the lab assistant.

Grading

Specific grading information will be provided by your instructor. The typical requirements of an electric circuits lab course includes a lab notebook, and at least one formal lab report. A lab exam may also be given. Typical formats for lab notebooks and a formal lab reports are presented on the following pages.

Lab Notebook Procedures

Laboratory experiments should be recorded in a notebook which is square-ruled with approximately five lines per inch. The notebooks should be bound (not loose leaf or spiral). They should be orderly and complete.

Data from the experiment should be recorded directly into the notebook. It is a good idea to prepare the data tables before coming to the lab. It may be acceptable to use pencil; however, many organizations require that a pen be used for official notebooks. If a computer printout or other addendum is specifically required to be attached to your notebook, it should be thoroughly taped on all edges in the book. Do not staple in your book.

The laboratory notebook is a record of what happened in the laboratory. The significance of any measurement, calculation, or observation made during the course of the experiment may not be apparent until the experiment is completed. Therefore, the lab notebook should contain all the measurements and observations.

Each experiment should include the following:

1. The experiment number and title.
2. Statement of purpose.
3. Parts and equipment used.
4. Schematics and/or drawings.
5. Data tables for recording experimental results.
6. Graphs, curves or additional tables that may be needed.
7. Analysis and conclusions.

You will be using computer spreadsheets to analyze and organize your data and results. Do not record your measurements directly into the spreadsheet program. Copy your measurements from your lab notebook into the spreadsheet. Keep your notebook as neat and well organized as possible.

In some cases, you may need specific information about the test instruments. For example, you may need to know the internal resistance of a measuring instrument, or the specific settings of the instrument. Be sure to record all of the information that you may need.

Specific lab notebook procedures will be provided by the lab instructor.

Formal Lab Report

At least one written formal report may be required. The instructor will specify which experiment or experiments may require a formal report. The general format for the formal report is given below. Each report should be organized into clearly defined and labeled sections which include the following:

1. Abstract
2. Introduction or problem statement.
3. Experimental setup and procedure.
4. Results and discussion.
5. Conclusions.

The exact organization depends on the experiment. Some experiments may have several parts, and each part may require a separate introduction, procedure, and results section. In some cases, an appendix may be needed. Additional information and suggestions on the content of each section are presented below.

1. *Abstract:* A short summary of the purpose, methods, and results of the experiment. Often just one paragraph is needed. It is usually written last (after you have a good idea of what the experiment was about and what actually happened).

2. *Introduction or problem statement:* A clearly stated explanation of the experiment. State the purpose of the experiment.

3. *Experimental setup and procedure:* Circuit diagrams, equipment used, measurement methods, drawings, etc., as needed.

4. *Results and discussion:* A tabulation of the measurements made with tables and graphs, as needed. Comparison to theoretical expectation which may include calculations and computer simulations. A statistical analysis, percent deviation of the results from the theoretical, which may include graphs and a spreadsheet analysis. A discussion of the results, including possible causes of errors, etc.

5. Conclusions: A short summary of the results, significance of the results, comments on the results. It usually takes experience to write a good conclusion.

You may want to include an appendix containing references cited in the report, such as the manufacturers' data sheets on parts used, or information on the instruments used in the experiment. A typical formal lab report may be between 5 and 10 pages long and include diagrams, graphs, and tables. It must be done using a word processor. Diagrams, tables and graphs should be imported directly into the word processor, using for example, the "clipboard" in Microsoft Windows. Being able to use software, such as word processors, spreadsheets, and engineering design and simulation tools is becoming more and more important.

A2: Phase Tripler Circuit Information

Description

This phase tripler circuit converts single-phase 60 Hz AC to three-phase 60 Hz AC using just two simple phase shift networks. The single-phase source may be a function generator or the AC voltage from a step down transformer.

The maximum input amplitude is 20 V peak-to-peak. The output amplitude is the same as the input. The diagram on the left below shows three-phase AC produced by three sources connected in a 4-wire wye configuration. A block diagram of the phase tripler circuit is shown below on the right.

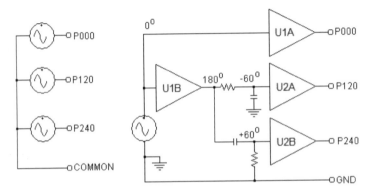

The zero degree reference source is buffered by the op-amp, U1A, and output at P000. An op-amp phase inverter, U1B, shifts the phase of the input by 180 degrees. This phase shifted voltage is applied to a 60 degree lag network to obtain a net phase shift of 120 degrees, and to a 60 degree lead network to obtain a net phase shift of 240 degrees.

The magnitude of the voltage output by these networks is one half of the input, so op-amps, U2A and U2B, are used to amplify the voltage by a factor of two. The 120 degree and 240 degree voltages are output at P120 and P240 with the same amplitude as the voltage at output P000. Trimmer potentiometers are used to adjust the phase and amplitudes of the outputs.

This is a wye-connected source with a common connection that is also the circuit ground for the power supply and op-amps. Instrument grounds cannot be connected to the output of an op-amp because that would cause a short circuit.

Measurements should be made with respect to the common ground, unless the measuring instrument is known to be isolated from ground.

The recommended maximum load current for each output is 40 mA. At 20 V peak-to-peak, this corresponds to 280 mW per output. The impedance of any load connected to an output should not be less than 175 Ω. Also, the very low output impedance of the op-amps contributes to excellent load regulation for loads greater than 175 Ω.

Construction

This circuit may be built on a breadboard, or a printed circuit board can be obtained from www.zapstudio.com.

The circuit is designed to operate at 60 Hz only. Other frequencies will not produce the correct phase angles. 60 Hz was chosen to correspond to the power distribution frequency in the USA.

It is also possible to use a 117VAC to 6.3VAC step-down transformer as a signal source instead of a function generator. But the transformer waveform may be somewhat distorted and noisy.

Calibration Procedure

1. The circuit board layout of the phase tripler is shown on the right. This one uses banana plug type binding posts for the power supply and output connections. A BNC type connector is used for the 60 Hz input.

    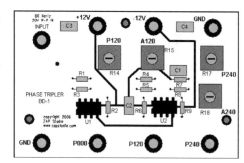

    It's also possible to have a circuit board with wires instead of binding posts (saves money and assembly time).

    The circuit may also be on a breadboard.

    Connect a 1K, ¼ watt resistor between each output and ground. Connect +12 V to the +12V connector and –12 V to the –12V connector. Connect the power supply ground to the phase tripler ground.

    Connect a function generator to the input and set it to produce a 12-volt peak-to-peak, 60Hz, sine wave.

2. Connect the oscilloscope channel 1 to output P000. The output at P000 should be exactly 12 V peak-to-peak at 60 Hz. Set the trigger to channel 1. Connect channel 2 of the oscilloscope to output P240.

3. Set the oscilloscope time base to 1 mS per division. Center both traces. Adjust R17 so that the positive slope P240 zero crossing is exactly 5.56 mS after the positive slope P000 zero crossing.

    Adjust R18 so that the amplitude of P240 output is exactly 12 V peak-to-peak.

4. Connect the oscilloscope channel 2 to output P120. Set the oscilloscope time base to 2.5 mS per division (or 2 mS per division). Center both traces. Adjust R14 so that the positive slope P120 zero crossing is exactly 11.11 mS after the positive slope P000 zero crossing.

    Adjust R15 so that the amplitude of P120 output is exactly 12 V peak-to-peak.

The graphs on the right show a rotating phasor diagram and the resulting sinusoids.

This corresponds to the ACB phase sequence generated by the phase tripler.

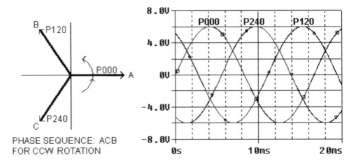

PHASE SEQUENCE: ACB
FOR CCW ROTATION

Circuit Schematic Diagram

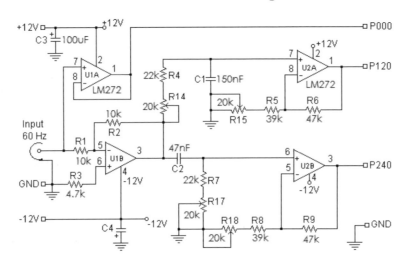

Parts List

U1, U2: L272M (Mouser 512-L272M) power op-amps.
R14, R15, R17, R18: 20K trim-pots (Mouser 652-3386P-1-203).
R1, R2: 10K, ¼, 5%.   R3: 4.7K, ¼ watt, 5%.   R4, R7: 22K, ¼ watt, 5%.
R5, R8: 39K, ¼ watt, 5%.   R6, R9: 47K, ¼ watt, 5%.
C1: 150 nF, 5%.   C2: 47 nF, 5%   C3, C4: 100 µF.
J1: BNC panel jack (Mouser 530-CP-1094-U).
7 banana jacks/binding posts.

Note: Wire connections or pins could be used instead of the binding posts and BNC connector.

The picture on the right shows the Phase Tripler as assembled for Portland Community College.

The bare printed circuit board is available from ZAP Studio LLC. www.zapstudio.com
Assembled and tested boards may also be available for quantity purchase.

A3: Data Logging with a Tektronix TDS Oscilloscope

1. Open Excel. You should see the TekXL tool bar as shown on the right. Click on "connection".

2. Select an instrument, usually the first one, and click on "identify". The instrument ID should appear at the bottom of the window, in this case, "TDS1002".

   Click "OK". If there is a problem with this part of the procedure, ask the instructor or lab assistant for help. Also, you may click on the "Help" in the TekXL tool bar.

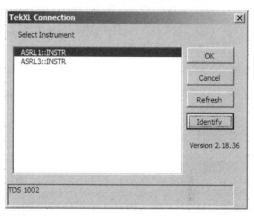

3. Click on "Measurements" in the TekXL tool bar. Click the "Selection" tab and select both channels. Select the measurements to be made.

4. Click on the "Timing" tab. Select "Set Capture to Start" to "Immediately". Set capture interval. Set record length.

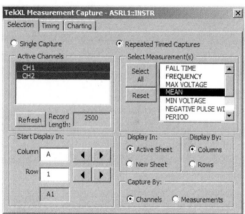

5. Click on the "Charting" tab.
   Set chart options and percentage interval.

6. Click on "RUN" when ready to capture data.

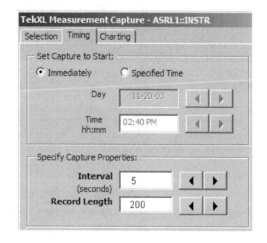

A4: PSPICE Example / FFT Simulation of a Pulse

OrCad PSpice FFT was used to obtain the spectra below.
Pulse width = 1 second.   Amplitude = 1 volt. Rise time = 1 μs.
Fall time = 1 μs. The effect of increasing the period is shown for
periods of 2 seconds, 10 seconds, and 100 seconds.

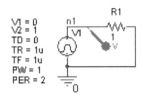

Simulation type = transient. Maximum step size = 1ms. Simulation time was set to obtain 64 pulses in the time domain. FFT plot frequency range was limited to 6.4 Hz (Click on "Plot" in the Probe window and select "Axis Settings" and set the user defined data range upper frequency to 6.4 Hz).

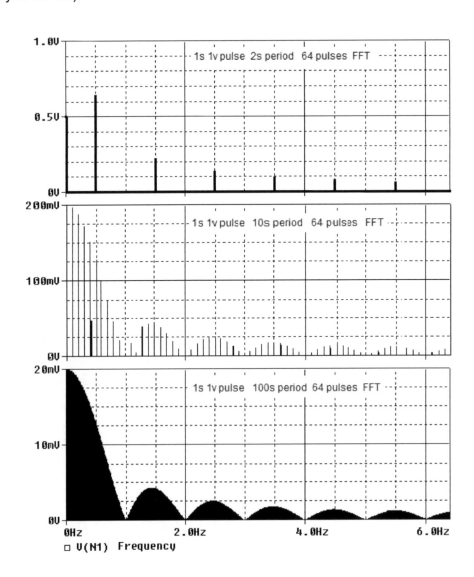

A5: Maple Example / Analysis of the Series RLC Circuit

Natural Response

An analysis of the natural response of a series RLC circuit is presented here. R = 920 Ω, L = 10 mH, and C = 1 nF. Starting with the differential equation of the circuit which is obtained from Kirchhoff's Voltage Law (mesh current method), and an initial charge on the capacitor of 5.00 volts, we first solve the differential equation using *Maple*. Refer to a circuits textbook, such as: *Electric Circuits* by *Nilsson and Reidell*, for information on writing the equations and evaluating the initial conditions.

Current in the circuit on the right is due to the capacitor discharging from an initial charge of 5 volts at t = 0.

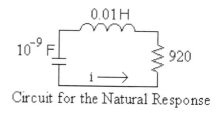

Circuit for the Natural Response

Differential Equation Method:

> deq:=diff(i(t),t,t)+92000.0*diff(i(t),t)+(1*10^11)*i(t)=0;

$$deq := \left(\frac{\partial^2}{\partial t^2} i(t)\right) + 92000\left(\frac{\partial}{\partial t} i(t)\right) + 100000000000 i(t) = 0$$

> dsolve({deq, i(0)=0, D(i)(0)=500}, i(t));

$$i := .001598 e^{(-46000t)} \sin(312864t)$$

> restart;

Note: When editing the equations above, such as changing the initial conditions, errors may occur upon execution, even if there are no errors in the statements. Often the statements will be executed correctly by executing the "restart" command, and then using "execute > worksheet" in the edit menu.

The 920 Ω in the above circuit represents the series resistance of the inductor, function generator, and external resistor, Rx. Polarity of the voltage across the 920 Ω due to i(t) would be negative at the top of the resistor with respect to the bottom for the first half cycle of $\sin(\omega_d t)$.

Laplace Transform Method:

It is usually easier to convert a circuit into the "s-domain" and to write an s-domain equation from the s-domain circuit than it is to describe the circuit by differential equations. *Maple* is useful in circuit analysis in solving an s-domain equation for a particular variable, and converting the equation to the time-domain. The s-domain circuit is shown below.

Input the s-domain equation for the circuit into Maple. Results are shown below. Current is represented by the Laplace variable, Y, because in Maple, $I = \sqrt{1}$. The 920 Ω resistance is the sum of the internal resistance of the function generator, the inductor, and 800 Ω.

> ith(inttrans):Leq:=920.0*Y+0.01*s*Y+(1*10^9/s)*Y-5/s=0;

$$Leq := 920Y + .01s + 1000000000\frac{Y}{s} - \frac{5}{s} = 0$$

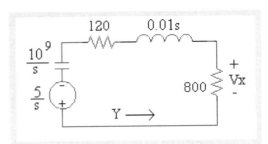

> LY:=solve(Leq,Y);

$$LY := \frac{500}{92000s + s^2 + .10000 \cdot 10^{12}}$$

> i:=invlaplace(LY,s,t);

$$i := .001598e^{(-46000t)} \sin(312864t)$$

> plot(i,t=0..0.0001);

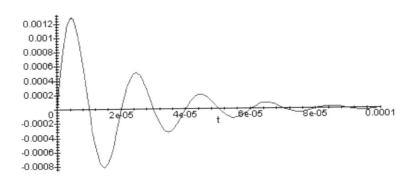

Sinusoidal Steady State Response

A steady state sinusoidal voltage applied to an RLC circuit results in a steady state sinusoidal current. This current is maximum at resonance for a series RLC circuit. The bandwidth of the circuit can be calculated to be the difference in the two frequencies where the magnitude of the current is $1/\sqrt{2}$ of what it is at resonance. Phasor analysis may be used to calculate the response.

Maple Solution:

> R:=920: L:=0.01: C:=1*10^(-9): XL:=w*L: XC:= 1/(w*C): Is:=(10.0/(R+I*(XL-XC)));

$$Is := \frac{10}{920 + I\left(.01w - \dfrac{1000000000}{w}\right)}$$

> eq1:=XL-XC=0:
> wo:=solve(eq1,w);

   wo := -316227.7660, 316227.7660

> Iso:=subs(w=316227.766,Is);

   Iso := .01086956522

> BW:=R/L;

Iso is the peak to peak current in the circuit at the resonant frequency, wo. Frequencies are in radians per second.

   BW := 92000.00000

Comments:

Results above indicate that the resonant frequency is 316,228 radians per second. Bandwidth is 92,000 radians per second. The bandwidth and the damping rate of the circuit can be shown to be related as: BW = 2α.

The resonant frequency calculated by *Maple*, above, is the natural resonant frequency, which may be calculated from:

$$\omega_0 = \frac{1}{\sqrt{LC}}$$

The damped oscillating frequency is related to the natural resonant frequency and the damping rate by the equation:

$$\omega_d = \sqrt{\omega_0^2 - \alpha^2}$$

A6: Maple Example / Series RLC Circuit Impulse Response

The circuit on the right is analyzed using Maple's Laplace transform capability. First the circuit's transfer function is obtained by using the voltage divider equation in the s-domain.

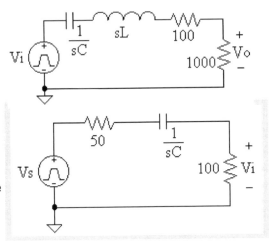

Next the strength of the exponential source, Vi, is approximated as an impulse function whose strength is the area under the voltage versus time curve of the exponential function. The function's rise time is assumed to be negligible. The amplitude of Vi used here is 6.5 volts, and the decay rate is 8,333,000.

```
> L:=.01:  C:=1.0*10^(-9):
> with(inttrans): H:=1000/(1100+s*L+(1/(s*C)));
```

$$H := \frac{1000}{1100 + .01s + \dfrac{.1000 \cdot 10^{10}}{s}}$$

```
> S:=6.5*int(exp(-8333000*t),t=0..infinity);
```

$$S := .78003 \cdot 10^{-6}$$

```
> Vo:=H*S;
```

$$Vo := \frac{.00078003}{1100 + .01s + \dfrac{.1000 \cdot 10^{10}}{s}}$$

```
> v:=invlaplace(Vo,s,t);
```

$$v := .078003e^{(-55000t)} \cos(311408t) - .01377e^{(-55000t)} \sin(311408t)$$

```
> plot(v,t=0..100*10^(-6));
```

A plot of the RLC circuit impulse response is shown above on the right. V is in volts as a function of time in seconds.

206

Step Response of the Impulse Generating Circuit

> C1:=1.0*10^(-9):vs:=10.0*Heaviside(t):

> with(inttrans):H1:=100/(150+(1/(s*C1)));

$$H1 := \frac{100}{\left(150 + \dfrac{.1000 \cdot 10^{10}}{s}\right)}$$

>Vs:=laplace(vs,t,s);

$$Vs := \frac{10}{s}$$

> Vi:=H1*Vs;

$$Vi := \frac{1000}{\left(150 + \dfrac{.1000 \cdot 10^{10}}{s}\right)s}$$

> vi:=invlaplace(Vi,s,t);

$$vi := 6.6666e^{(-.6666 \cdot 10^7\, t)}$$

> plot(vi,t=0..1*10^(-6));

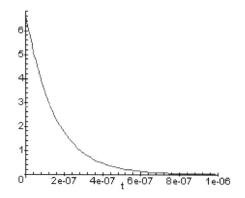

207

A7: MATLAB Example / RLC Resonant Response

The example below shows the utility of the "anonymous function".

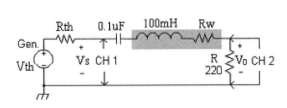

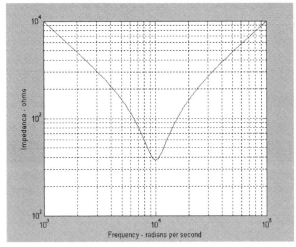

$$Z = 370 + j(.1\omega - \frac{10^7}{\omega})$$

```
>> Z = @(w) abs(370+j*(.1*w-10^7/w));

>> fplot(Z,[1000 1E5])
```

The syntax for creating an anonymous function from an expression is
fhandle = @(arglist) expr.

Starting from the right of this syntax statement, the term "expr" represents the body of the function: the code that performs the main task your function is to accomplish. This consists of any single, valid MATLAB expression.

Next is "arglist", which is a comma-separated list of input arguments to be passed to the function. These two components are similar to the body and argument list components of any function.

Leading off the entire right side of this statement is an @ sign. The @ sign is the MATLAB operator that constructs a function handle. Creating a function handle for an anonymous function gives you a means of invoking the function. It is also useful when you want to pass your anonymous function in a call to some other function. The @ sign is a required part of an anonymous function definition.

A8: MATLAB Example / RLC Step Response

The example below is solved in the s-domain:

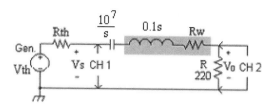

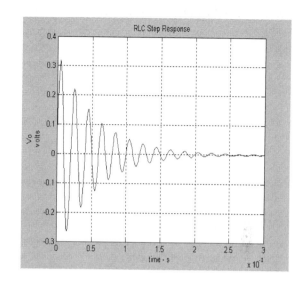

syms s t

Z=370+10E7/s+.1*s;

V1=(220/Z)*5/s;

V2=ilaplace(V1);

vpa(V2,4)

   ans =

  .3484*exp(-1850.*t)*sin(.3156e5*t)

Vo=@(t).3484*exp(-1850.*t)*sin(.3156e5*t);

fplot(Vo,[0 3E-3])

The circuit impedance, Z, is in the s-domain. V1 is the a product of the circuit's transfer function (220/Z) and the input voltage (5/s). V2 is the inverse laplace of V1. V2 is approximated to 4 digits. Vo is made an "anonymous function" of V2 and plotted using "fplot".

A9: *TI-89* and S-Domain Pulse Response with *MATLAB* and *Maple* Plots

Simulation results of the circuit below are shown on the right. The voltage at node N1 approaches 5 volts exponentially in 10 milliseconds. The voltage at node N2 reaches a peak value of 1.4 volts in one millisecond and then decays exponentially.

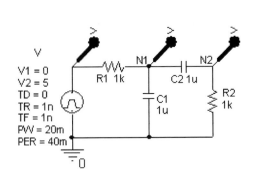

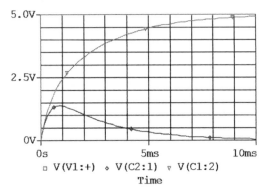

S-domain node voltage equations for nodes N1 and N2 are:

$$\dfrac{V1-\dfrac{5}{s}}{1000}+\dfrac{V1}{\dfrac{1E6}{s}}+\dfrac{V1-V2}{\dfrac{1E6}{s}}=0 \quad \text{and} \quad \dfrac{V2-V1}{\dfrac{1E6}{s}}+\dfrac{V2}{1000}=0$$

Enter the equations into the *TI-89* as follows (V1 = x, V2 = y):

solve((x − 5/s)/1000 + x/(1E6/s) + (x − y)/(1E6/s) = 0 and (y − x)/(1E6/s) + y/1000 = 0, {x,y})

$$x=\dfrac{5E3(s+1E3)}{s(s^2+3E3s+1E6)} \quad \text{and} \quad y=\dfrac{5E3}{s^2+3E3s+1E6}$$

Using the "expand" command to expand the equation for y just returned the same equation. The roots of the denominator are s = -381 and s = -2618. Therefore V2, which is the expression for y, can be written as:

$$V2=\dfrac{K1}{s+381}+\dfrac{K2}{s+2618} \qquad K1=\dfrac{5000}{-381+2618}=2.235 \quad \text{and} \quad K2=\dfrac{5000}{-2618+381}=-2.235$$

The inverse transform gives: $v2=2.235e^{-381t}-2.235e^{-2618t}$

$V2 = 2.235e^{-381t} - 2.235e^{-2618\,t}$

MATLAB was used to produce the plot on the right. Note that the results match the simulation.

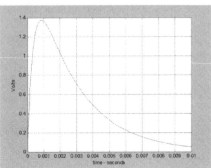

```
>> v2 = @(t) 2.235*exp(-381*t)-2.235*exp(-2618*t);
>> fplot(v2,[0 0.01])
```

Solve for V1:

$$V1 = V2 + \frac{5 \times 10^6}{s(s+381)(s+2618)} = V2 + \frac{Ka}{s} + \frac{Kb}{(s+381)} + \frac{Kc}{(s+2618)}$$

$$Ka = \frac{5 \times 10^6}{381 \times 2618} \qquad Kb = \frac{5 \times 10^6}{-381 \times (2618 - 381)} \qquad Kc = \frac{5 \times 10^6}{-2618 \times (-2618 + 381)}$$

Ka = 5.0125   Kb = -5.8665   Kc = .8538

$V1 = 2.235e^{-381t} - 2.235e^{-2618t} + 5.0125 - 5.8665\,e^{-381t} + .8538\,e^{-2618t}$

$V1 = 5.0125 - 3.6315\,e^{-381t} - 1.3812\,e^{-2618t}$

Maple plot of V1:

```
> plot(5.0125-3.6315*exp(-381*t)-1.3812*exp(-2618*t),t=0..0.01);
```

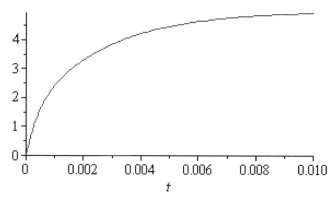

V1 in Volts vs. Time in Seconds

A10: Math Reference

Taylor Series

Taylor's Theorem is commonly used to approximate functions. The Taylor Series expansion, $f_T(x)$, of the function, $f(x)$, about a point, x_0, is given by:

$$f_T(x) = f(x_0)\Big|_{x=0} + (x - x_0) \frac{df(x)}{dx}\Big|_{x=0} + \frac{(x - x_0)^2}{2!} \frac{d^2f(x)}{dx^2}\Big|_{x=0} + \frac{(x - x_0)^3}{3!} \frac{d^3f(x)}{dx^3}\Big|_{x=0} + \dots$$

Example:

$$f(x) = Ae^{-kx} = A \quad \text{at } x = 0.$$

$$\frac{df(x)}{dx} = -kAe^{-kx} = -kA \quad \text{at } x = 0.$$

$$\frac{d^2f(x)}{dx^2} = k^2Ae^{-kx} = k^2A \quad \text{at } x = 0.$$

$$\frac{d^3f(x)}{dx^3} = -k^3Ae^{-kx} = -k^3A \quad \text{at } x = 0.$$

If $A = k = 1$, the first 4 terms of $f_T(x)$ expanded about $x = 0$ are:

$$f_T(x) = 1 - x + \frac{1}{2}x^2 - \frac{1}{6}x^3$$

Compare results of $[f(x) = e^{-x}]$ and $[f_T(x) = 1 - x + \frac{1}{2}x^2 - \frac{1}{6}x^3]$ at $x = 1$.
$f(1) = 0.36788$ and $f_T(1) = .33333$. The error = 9.4%.

Useful Trigonometry

$$\sin(A \pm B) = \sin A \cos B \pm \cos A \sin B$$

$$\cos(A \pm B) = \cos A \cos B \mp \sin A \sin B$$

$$\cos \omega t = \sin(\omega t + 90^o) \qquad \sin \omega t = \cos(\omega t - 90^o)$$

$$e^{j\theta} = \cos \theta + j \sin \theta \qquad e^{-j\theta} = \cos \theta - j \sin \theta$$

212

Basic Calculus

$$a = \text{constant} \qquad u = f(x) \qquad v = f(x)$$

$$\frac{d}{dx}a=0 \qquad \frac{d}{dx}x=1 \qquad \frac{d}{dx}ax=a \qquad \int adx=ax$$

$$\frac{d}{dx}x^n=nx^{n-1} \qquad \int x^n dx=\frac{1}{n+1}x^{n+1}$$

$$\frac{d}{dx}e^{ax}=ae^{ax} \qquad \int e^{ax} dx=\frac{1}{a}e^{ax}$$

$$\frac{d}{dx}\ln x=\frac{1}{x} \qquad \int \frac{1}{x}dx=\ln x$$

$$\frac{d}{dx}\sin ax=a\cos ax \qquad \int \cos ax dx=\frac{1}{a}\sin ax$$

$$\frac{d}{dx}\cos ax=-a\sin ax \qquad \int \sin ax dx=-\frac{1}{a}\cos ax$$

$$\frac{d}{dx}uv=u\frac{dv}{dx}+v\frac{du}{dx} \qquad \int udv=uv-\int vdu$$

Useful Integrals

$$\int xe^{ax}dx = \frac{e^{ax}}{a^2}(ax-1)$$

$$\int x^2 e^{ax}dx = \frac{e^{ax}}{a^2}\left(a^2 x^2 - 2ax + 2\right)$$

$$\int e^{ax}\sin bx\,dx = \frac{e^{ax}}{a^2+b^2}\left(a\sin bx - b\cos bx\right)$$

$$\int e^{ax}\cos bx\,dx = \frac{e^{ax}}{a^2+b^2}\left(a\cos bx + b\sin bx\right)$$

$$\int x\sin ax\,dx = \frac{1}{a^2}\sin ax - \frac{x}{a}\cos ax$$

$$\int x\cos ax\,dx = \frac{1}{a^2}\cos ax + \frac{x}{a}\sin ax$$

$$\int \frac{1}{x^2+a^2}dx = \frac{1}{a}\tan^{-1}\frac{x}{a}$$

$$\int \sin^2 ax\,dx = \frac{x}{2} - \frac{\sin 2ax}{4a}$$

$$\int \cos^2 ax\,dx = \frac{x}{2} + \frac{\sin 2ax}{4a}$$

Laplace Transforms

$\delta(t)$	1
$u(t)$	$\dfrac{1}{s}$
$tu(t)$	$\dfrac{1}{s^2}$
$e^{-at}u(t)$	$\dfrac{1}{s+a}$
$\sin\omega t\,u(t)$	$\dfrac{\omega}{s^2+\omega^2}$
$\cos\omega t\,u(t)$	$\dfrac{s}{s^2+\omega^2}$
$te^{-at}u(t)$	$\dfrac{1}{(s+a)^2}$
$e^{-at}\sin\omega t\,u(t)$	$\dfrac{\omega}{(s+a)^2+\omega^2}$
$e^{-at}\cos\omega t\,u(t)$	$\dfrac{s+a}{(s+a)^2+\omega^2}$
$2|A|e^{-\alpha t}\cos(\beta t+\theta)u(t)$	$\dfrac{A}{s+\alpha-j\beta}+\dfrac{A^*}{s+\alpha+j\beta}$

215

Operational Laplace Transforms

$$A f(t) \qquad\qquad\qquad A F(s)$$

$$f_1(t)+f_2(t) \qquad\qquad F_1(s)+F_2(s)$$

$$\frac{d}{dt}f(t) \qquad\qquad s F(s)-f(0^-)$$

$$\frac{d^2}{dt^2}f(t) \qquad\qquad s^2 F(s)-s f(0^-)-f(0^-)$$

$$\int_0^t f(\tau)d\tau \qquad\qquad \frac{F(s)}{s}$$

$$e^{-at}f(t) \qquad\qquad F(s+a)$$

$$t f(t) \qquad\qquad -\frac{d}{ds}F(s)$$

$$t^2 f(t) \qquad\qquad \frac{d^2}{ds^2}F(s)$$

$$t^{-1}f(t) \qquad\qquad \int_0^\infty F(x)dx$$

$$f(at),\, a>0 \qquad\qquad \frac{1}{a}F\left(\frac{s}{a}\right)$$

$$f(t-a)u(t-a),\, a>0 \qquad e^{-as}F(s)$$

66191440R00124

Made in the USA
San Bernardino, CA
09 January 2018